THE CR

Fred Secombe was born in Swansea and ordained in 1942. The vicar of various parishes and a Prebendary of St Paul's Cathedral, he is also the founder of three Gilbert & Sullivan Companies and won the Waterford International Festival of Light Opera Award for *Utopia Ltd* in 1968. He now lives in Cardiff.

The Crowning Glory

FRED SECOMBE

Illustrated by Maxine Rogers

Fount

An Imprint of HarperCollins*Publishers*

Fount Paperbacks is an Imprint of
HarperCollins*Religious*
Part of HarperCollins*Publishers*
77–85 Fulham Palace Road, London W6 8JB

First published in Great Britain
in 1995 by Michael Joseph Ltd
This edition published in 1996 by Fount Paperbacks

5 7 9 10 8 6 4

A catalogue record for this book is
available from the British Library

ISBN 000 627985-6

Printed and bound in Great Britain by
Caledonian International Book Manufacturering, Scotland

To my grandchildren, Elena, Hannah, Gwyn and Nicholas, in the hope that the post Elizabethan era will produce a better world.

'I don't see any need for this meeting at all.' Bertie Owen, shop steward and deposed churchwarden, was on his feet amidst groans and sighs from his listeners. 'Tabernacle, Bethel, Moriah are doing nothing at all and don't forget that "Tab" give their Sunday School an outing to Porthcawl, not out to the cowfield like we do. They say that their kids will be going to the street parties. Balaclava, Sebastopol, Inkerman have got their celebrations arranged, not to mention Alma and Delhi.'

'Before you run through any more battles, Mr Owen, would you mind sitting down for a moment,' I said, to a chorus of 'Hear! Hear!s' 'I am fully aware of the many street parties which are being organised. There is no earthly reason why our Sunday-school children should not be able to attend them and also take part in whatever we as a Parochial Church Council can provide for them. In any case I hope we shall be able to put on entertainment for the grown-ups as well.'

It was the first meeting of the newly elected Council after the Easter Vestry on Low Sunday 1953. The whole country was agog with excitement at the prospect of the forthcoming coronation of the second Elizabeth on 2 June. Already there was talk of a new Elizabethan age. For too long the nation had been shackled by the austerity of the post-war regime. The chains had been loosened by the Festival of Britain in 1951 but rationing still lingered on and the word 'control' was the most detestable in the current vocabulary.

I had now been Vicar of Pontywen for nearly five years, with a three-year-old son, David, and a six-month-old baby daughter, Elspeth. My wife, Eleanor, the local doctor, was fortunate to have David Andrews as her partner in the practice. He had come to the town after service in the RAMC and had been an immediate success with his ability to diagnose and with the sympathetic manner which accompanied the diagnosis. His wife, Heather, had given birth to their first child, a baby girl on Easter Day. Both mother and child were doing well.

'What I had in mind', I went on, 'is a full programme of events both for the children and the adults. A "go as you please" variety competition in the church hall for young and old. A dance, a whist drive. That sort of thing. Mrs Heather Andrews hopes to be back in harness after the birth of baby Christine by 2 June and says that she would like to give pony rides for the children. I am sure that you all have many more ideas about how we can enjoy ourselves to celebrate this historic day.'

As soon as I sat down, David Vaughan-Jenkins, people's churchwarden at the parish church and local bank manager, took the floor. 'May I say, Vicar, that I am sure your proposals will have our fullest support (Hear! hear!). How kind of Mrs Andrews to offer the use of her pony for rides for the children. I think, perhaps, Vicar, you should have said that she hopes to be back "with harness", rather than "in harness".' He paused to allow for laughter or at least some audible appreciation of his heavy-handed humour. None came. He coughed and proceeded with his peroration. 'Might I suggest that

2

we elect some kind of Coronation Celebrations Committee who will co-ordinate activities after we have had contributions from the meeting suggesting other things that might be done. Mr Bertie Owen has informed us that other places of worship are doing nothing to mark the occasion. I suggest that they join us in our activities on such a committee. One other thing, I shall contact headquarters to see whether the bank may make a donation towards the cost of the festivity. If ever there is a worthy cause, I am sure this is it.' This time his remarks were greeted with hearty applause.

Next on his feet was Idris Shoemaker, alias 'Idris the Milk', people's warden at St Padarn's, the daughter church. 'I would like to second Mr Vaughan-Jenkins's proposition about a committee to organise the events and to support his idea about the Chapels combining with us. Mind, I don't think Moriah Baptist will be too keen on a whist drive or a dance.'

'Before we go h'any further,' intervened Ezekiel Evans, the parochial lay reader. 'Might h'I suggest that we h'invite h'all the other places of worship in Pontywen to join us in an h'act of prayer h'and dedication. Old Canon Williams in h'our cathedral last Sunday said we could be h'embarking on a new h'age of religious revival and denominational 'armony. First things first. Never mind about h'enjoying ourselves and all that.'

'May I echo Mr Evans's words,' I said. The lay reader's face was a picture of self-satisfaction. 'By that I mean – "before we go any further". The purpose of this meeting is to arrange a programme of festivities to celebrate the coronation of our new monarch. It is not to promote a religious revival in Pontywen.' The smile vanished from

Ezekiel's face. 'Quite frankly I see no point whatsoever in asking all the other places of worship, as Mr Evans put it, to join us for a service or for a week of fun and frolic. I doubt if they would agree to a united service on our terms and I am positive that they would not wish to be involved in fun and frolic.

'In any case, by the time we had organised an interdenominational committee and debated what form of service we should have and where it should be held and who would take part etcetera, the coronation would have taken place weeks earlier. As for the fun and frolic aspect, that is a non starter. However, if you wish to go ahead and vote on the proposition before you, please do so.'

As soon as I sat down, David Vaughan-Jenkins was on his feet. As a bank manager, he was a pragmatist. He withdrew his proposition, with the enthusiastic support of his seconder, who realised that the proposer had unwittingly led the meeting up a blind alley. From that moment, the meeting proceeded to manufacture ideas for entertainment at such a speed that Miss Alice Worthington, secretary to the Council and secretary to the Colliery Manager, found her shorthand ability put to the test.

The people's warden at the parish church was on his feet once again. 'I revert to my original proposition, omitting references to other places of worship. In other words, I propose that we the church people of Pontywen elect a committee to organise coronation festivities to mark the occasion. I further suggest that we include the parish of Llanhyfryd and their representatives on that committee.' This was seconded by Idris, who had second thoughts about Moriah and Bethel joining us to arrange a week of pleasurable activity. The motion was carried, with only one vote against, that of a sulking Ezekiel Evans. Even Bertie Owen voted in favour, not wishing to be left out of the picture and hoping that there might be a place for him on the organising committee. However, the eight names of the elected did not include his, bringing the number of those sulking up to two.

An interested spectator of the meeting was Emlyn Howells, my new curate, who had joined me some days previously from a curacy in Aberllynfi, a small market town in the neighbouring diocese. An ex 'Bevin Boy', his health had been seriously affected by his work underground. Part of one lung had been removed, leaving him with breathing difficulties on occasions. He was stoutly built, with a ruddy complexion belying his physical condition. An open-air enthusiast after his mining experience, he was a keen camper. At the interview prior to his appointment he had asked me whether he might form a scout troop in the parish, a suggestion I welcomed gladly since my two previous curates would have found difficulty lighting a camp fire with matches let alone doing so by rubbing two sticks together. It would appear that for the first time since I had become an incumbent I would have an assistant who would assist instead of hindering.

As we left the hall together after the meeting I asked him what he thought of the evening's business. 'I must say that I was most impressed by the way in which everybody produced ideas for the programme of events. If it had been my former parochial church council, the most they would have suggested would have been a tea party, and even that would have been badly organised. I suppose that is the difference between the countryside and the industrial valleys in the pace of life?'

'Very true, Emlyn,' I replied. 'You will see this when you attend a meeting at Llanhyfryd. Yet, even there, you will find plenty of suggestions coming from the members of the council. They have no wish to be outdone by the Pontywen crowd.'

'That is what competition can do for you,' said Emlyn. 'Perhaps they might have been more forthcoming in Aberllynfi if they were linked with another parish – though I doubt that very much.' He stopped abruptly as he was seized with a bout of coughing. 'Excuse me, a nasty tickle. I get that occasionally.

'One more thing, Vicar,' he went on; 'if you don't mind my saying so, it was good to see a chairman who was in command of the meeting and who knew where he was going. My last Vicar, dear man though he may have been, was obsessed with the idea that "we should be all of one mind", as he used to put it at every Church Council meeting. The result was that what should take an hour at the most became two hours or even three. So many liked the sound of their own voices. It's a wonder I never fell asleep.'

'I promise you, Emlyn,' I replied. 'Our PCC meetings will be too short for that to happen. I may be a bit of a closet dictator, in that I know what I want and am prepared to put down the self-important from their seat, but it saves time and it gets things done.'

When I was back at the Vicarage, Eleanor had just finished feeding Elspeth and was engaged in bringing up the baby's wind. She had insisted on breastfeeding the children despite the inconvenience it caused her as a busy GP. 'A mother's milk is much better for the health of a baby than the powdered product from a factory.'

She was bursting with excitement. 'What do you think? Your brother has phoned to say that he is sending us a television set so that we can watch the coronation.'

My brother, Harry, was now a radio celebrity in the 'Goon Show' as well as a stage success with his fine belcanto singing allied to his 'Goon' humour. Before he was called up as a Territorial Army Gunner just before his eighteenth birthday, he had taken part in amateur theatricals. My father, who was similarly involved as a reciter of comic monologues, had dismissed any idea of a stage career for my brother because he was of too nervous a disposition. After six years on active service, most of which was spent entertaining the troops (in between fighting the Germans), he had come home to Swansea, a seasoned performer. In no time at all he was engaged by Vivian Van Damm to do his 'shaving act' at the Windmill Theatre for the princely sum of twenty-five pounds a week. Six years later he was a comparatively wealthy man who could afford to send his brother a television set, a priceless possession in 1953 for someone living in the Valleys.

Later that evening, when the baby had been put in her cot for the night, we discussed the problem of compiling a complement of viewers for the great day. The Vicarage lounge was a big room but certainly not big enough to accommodate all those who would want to see the happenings. It would require the wisdom of Solomon to choose a suitable guest list and even he would have to offend a large number of the congregation.

'The only way to avoid contention', suggested Eleanor, 'is to keep it quiet that we have a television set.'

'That, my love, is impossible,' I replied. 'First of all we shall have to get Jones the Wireless to put it in for us, and you know what an old woman he is. Secondly, can you imagine Mrs Watkins keeping quiet about it. Let alone Marlene.'

Mrs Watkins was our 'daily' who had been indispensable to us since the birth of our children. Marlene Evans was one of the chorus of the church Gilbert and Sullivan society. She had become nursemaid to the children on leaving Pontywen Grammar school with a low-level academic record but with a much higher level of child care.

'In that case,' said my wife, 'our only hope is that one or two other members of the congregation will have installed television sets by the great day, and we can share the list of viewers. Perhaps David Vaughan-Jenkins will get one. Even if he does not want one, I am sure his wife will be asking to have such a mark of prestige. They have enough money, that's positive. What about the Nicholls? I bet they have a set already, the biggest you can buy. As Manager of the steelworks he has the only Rolls Royce in Pontywen. So I am sure that he will have the equivalent in television sets.'

'My dear love, since they come to St Mary's at Christmas and Easter only, I do not think you can class them as members of the congregation. They are twicers not members. Anyway I expect their drawing room will be occupied by golf-club friends and folk of that ilk.'

'I like the "ilk" bit, Fred. Still, I think it is worth a try. At least you will be able to boast that you are in the same league television wise, and that you are prepared to share

8

your good fortune with the peasants. You can promise to provide them with an approved selection of our best behaved worshippers who would not damage their carpets or their furniture.'

'Come off it, Eleanor. Ernest Nicholls is not at all like that. I admit that his wife comes into that category, as does her daughter, married as she is to Brigadier James Morris, Welsh Guards. Anyway I suppose any chance that Ernest would agree to sharing a view of the coronation with some of the St Mary's crowd would be overruled by the petticoat government of the rest of the household.'

'I suppose you are right, but you never know. If you get in now, perhaps you could persuade them that they would be contributing to the new age of Elizabeth the Second, a gesture to the proletariat that under our new Queen we shall be one nation with no divisions of race or class.'

'There's something wrong with your logic, Eleanor. You cannot mention the word proletariat and in the same breath declare that in this new Elizabethan age there will be no distinction of class. In any case I shouldn't think they would want an end to such a division. They are very happy with the difference between them and the working class. However, I shall venture forth tomorrow to Chez Nicholls to see what their reaction will be.'

The next morning I had a telephone call from the Reverend Daniel Thomas, the Rural Dean. 'I'm glad I've found you in, Vicar. It's like this. I'm in a bit of a hole. The Mothers' Union deanery service is going to be held in our church this afternoon. The Archdeacon was down to preach at the service, as you probably know. Well, he has just rung up to say that he has got laryngitis. I could hardly hear him over the phone. So I am sure that the ladies would never be able to hear him in the pulpit. I was wondering whether you would like to take his place. Use one of your old sermons. Don't put yourself out.'

Since I never wrote any sermons, I would have to 'put myself out'. At that moment I wished I had been like the vicar in my home parish. He had a twelve months' supply of written homilies which he would up-end on the last Sunday of the year and begin to preach all over again in the New Year. For example we always knew that on the Seventh Sunday after Trinity he would re-count how he had saved a child from drowning in the river near his home. Then on the thirteenth Sunday after Trinity, when the story of the Good Samaritan was the gospel for the day, we would be given details of the principal features of Jericho, together with a potted history and a geographical survey of the road to Jerusalem.

'It's very flattering of you to ask me to deputise for the Archdeacon, Mr Rural Dean. I shall do my best to be worthy of the honour.' My tongue was firmly in my cheek as I said it.

'That's good of you. There will be a tea afterwards in the church hall. Will Dr Sebohm be coming with you?' After I had been six years in the deanery, he could never get my name right.

'I am afraid she will be out on her rounds in the afternoon, much as she would like to be there.'

'A busy lady, I'm sure. Perhaps one of these days the two of you will come to tea with us and bring your children with you. My wife hasn't seen them yet and I am sure she would love to have them here. Anyway, we'll see you there at the service this afternoon. It is at three o'clock. Thank you once again.'

When I put the phone down I looked at the clock. It was a quarter past eleven. I had a couple of hours at most to compose the sermon. Before I had time to take my Bible commentary from the bookshelf the doorbell rang. There was a young couple on my doorstep. A handsome lad, he looked as if he was in his late teens and was shabbily dressed in trousers and a jacket which had seen better days. His open-necked shirt had not been near a wash tub for some time. His petite companion was even younger and was clad in a tent of a dress which bulged ominously around her waist line. It was she who spoke first. 'We've come to put our banns in, Vicar.' Her voice was firm and devoid of the Valleys intonation. She sounded as if she came from a middle-class background.

'You had better come in,' I said. 'I don't normally deal with banns of marriage at this time of the day but since you are here we might as well go ahead with the arrangements.'

I ushered them into the study where they seated themselves in the two armchairs in front of my desk. 'Mike is working the afternoon shift, you see, Vicar, and so we couldn't come this evening. As it is urgent, anyway, I hope you don't mind the intrusion.'

By now, I was intrigued by this relationship. I wondered what accent would come from the silent partner's lips. 'The first thing I have to ask you is your age. I may be wrong but I should judge by your youthful appearance that you are both under the age of twenty-one. In that case neither of you can be married without your parents' consent.' They bowed their heads. 'How old are you, Mike?'

He addressed the floor and spoke in a thick Valleys accent. 'Nineteen.'

I turned to the girl. 'Now then, my dear, what is your name?'

She raised her head and looked me full in the face. 'Margaret,' she replied.

'And how old are you?'

She dropped her head again and then raised it defiantly. 'Seventeen,' she said, her big blue eyes firmly fixed on mine.

'So then,' I went on. 'The first thing I have to ask is whether you have your parents' consent. Without their written consent I cannot call the banns of marriage. The second thing I have to say concerns you, Margaret. It is quite obvious that you are in an advanced stage of pregnancy. It will take a minimum of three weeks to have your banns called. You realise that? On the other hand, you could have a licence which could mean that it would be days rather than weeks. I am a surrogate and that means I could issue you with a licence.'

' 'Ow much would that cost?' enquired Mike.

'Three guineas,' I replied. 'However, most important of all at the moment is whether you have your parents' consent. Without that you can't be married.'

This time Mike spoke up. 'My mother and father are willing for us to get married. They've said we can 'ave a room with them until we find somewhere else. It's 'ers that are against it.'

Margaret's head had been bowed for some considerable time. 'Perhaps, my dear,' I said to her, 'you should let me know if your parents are prepared to give their consent to the marriage. If they are not, then there is no possibility whatever of a wedding. That is the law of the land. So do you have their consent or do you not?'

'If my parents are agreed that my child should be a bastard, it's up to them. I hope they will have it on their consciences for the rest of their lives.'

'In other words, Margaret, you have not had their permission.' She shook her head.

'What's more, my father wants to have me go to somewhere where I could have my baby adopted at the moral welfare place for unmarried mothers. I've told him I'm not going to do that.'

'There is one thing that puzzles me more than anything else, my dear, and that is why you want to get married in church rather than the registry office. I have never seen you in church.'

'You haven't seen me in church here, Vicar, because we have always gone to Penglais Parish Church. We moved to Pontywen two years ago, and my parents decided they would keep up the connection. I have been confirmed and have been to Communion regularly except over the past few months. If I am going to be married, then it will have to be in church.'

'Well now, I am afraid I cannot spend any more time with you at the moment. I have some urgent business on hand. Can I have your names and addresses, please? Then I shall contact your parents to see what can be done. First of all you, Mike.'

'Michael John Roberts, 13 Balaclava Street.'

'And you, Margaret?' There was a pause. She took a deep breath.

'Margaret Elaine Price, Raglan House, Ashburnham Close.'

'I shall see you both here on Friday evening at seven o'clock. In the meanwhile I shall be in touch with your parents.'

I watched them as they walked up the Vicarage drive. For young lovers they were strangely apart, no holding hands. Instead he was a stride ahead of her throughout the length of the drive, as wide apart as their addresses.

It took me half an hour to compose my thoughts sufficiently to begin work on my sermon to the Mothers' Union of the deanery, the large majority of whom would be grandmothers. I read through the accounts of the birth of Jesus in St Matthew and St Luke's gospels. St Matthew refers constantly to 'the young child and his mother'. Thinking of Margaret who was only seventeen, it seemed to me that shortly there would be two children in the Price family – a mother and her infant. Then reading through the Bible commentary I was reminded that probably Mary would have been only fourteen, a common age of espousal, three years younger than Margaret.

By the time Marlene came back to the Vicarage with our two children, whom she had taken to the Recreation ground for a fresh-air outing, it was half past twelve. She was followed closely by Eleanor, who had returned from her morning surgery and visits. She had made it a rule that her duties were confined to the morning, with the afternoon free for the children. Occasionally she would do an early-evening surgery, leaving David Andrews to cope single handed for most of the time.

'A nice afternoon for a drive into the country,' she said, as she came through the door.

'In which case you will have to count me out, I'm afraid,' I replied. 'Dear Mr Rural Dean has invited me to preach at the deanery Mothers' Union service because the Archdeacon has lost his voice.'

'His wife and his congregation will be pleased about that, even if you are not, by the look of you. Never mind, love. Think of that bevy of beauty facing you when you get up into the pulpit.'

'Eleanor, you are a wicked woman sometimes, thank God.'

As Marlene was leaving, I asked her if she had known Margaret Price in Pontywen Grammar School.

'I didn't know her very well because she came into our form just a term before I left. She had only just come to live in Pontywen from Penyglais. In any case, she kept herself to herself, didn't want to know us. She used to go to a private school once, so she said. I think her parents had plenty of money and used to spoil her. Her father used to come and pick her up sometimes in a posh car.'

'What was all that about?' Eleanor inquired after our nurserymaid had gone.

Over lunch I told her about the 'marriage interview' and their strange behaviour as they walked up the drive. 'She is certainly not one of my patients,' my wife said. 'I must ask David if she is one of his lot. She might be, especially since her parents live in the same road.'

'Anyway,' I replied, 'I am going to see them tomorrow, so if David can supply some information I shall be grateful.'

Pontywen Church was full for the Mothers' Union service when I arrived there. The banner carriers were outside the porch debating the order in which they were to march down the aisle. Inside the small vestry there was a crush of elderly clergymen already robed. In the middle of this clerical scrum was the Rural Dean looking 'like a fly trapped in a jam jar', to use one of Idris the Milk's favourite expressions.

'Thank goodness, you have come,' he exclaimed. 'I was beginning to think something had happened to you. Now then, gentlemen, if you don't mind, will you let me pass so that I can give the signal to the organist that we are ready? Come out in any order once I have said the vestry prayer, except of course that the preacher and I will be last.' He disappeared for a few seconds and then came back to the doorway. 'Let us pray,' he commanded. The vestry prayer was said at such a rate that it was unintelligible until the last few words, 'through Jesus Christ our Lord'. The organ began to play and the scramble to emerge into the chancel ensued, with the Rural Dean squashed against the vestry wall. I had taken the precaution of hiding behind the robes cupboard to escape injury.

'Come up into the sanctuary with me, Vicar,' said the dignitary. 'I will take the banners from the Mothers and hand them to you to prop up against the wall.' My heart sank. I had contended with these contraptions a year previously at a Mothers' Union festival in Pontywen. They had a habit of sliding on the polished floor as soon as you had turned your back.

During the singing of the hymn the procession moved up the aisle to the altar rails, led by a buxom lady, proudly carrying the banner belonging to the home territory. 'Thank you, Mrs Evans,' said the Rural Dean. 'Would you mind putting this one, Vicar, on that stand in the corner?' That was the easy part of the ceremony. There were six more banners to go. I tried to rest the next one against a memorial tablet to a former Vicar of Pentwyn, hoping to use the same manoeuvre on the other side with the following one. Evidently the late Emmanuel Hopkins felt his dignity impaired by being treated this way. After three attempts to prevent it sliding to the ground, I walked across the sanctuary and stuck it in the opposite corner to the banner of honour.

By now there was only one verse of the hymn to go and still five more banners to be laid against the walls. The Rural Dean was puffing his annoyance like a grampus whale and the strain of holding up the heavy Mothers' Union emblems was telling on their elderly bearers. 'Try to hurry up,' commanded the Reverend Daniel Thomas in the loudest of stage whispers. 'Put them anywhere but hurry up.'

As the singing of the last verse died away there were only two more left to be installed in the sanctuary. There was a space left for two on the north side. I took the first one and rested the pole against the altar rails: miraculously it stayed upright. As the sweat streamed down my forehead and gummed my shirt to my body under my robes, I advanced upon the last remaining empty space. Anxiously watched by a breathless audience of clergy, I laid the banner dedicated to St Mary's Abergwynlais MU against the wall. As I turned to rejoin the Rural Dean, I heard an ominous noise of a sliding pole which attracted the company of its neighbour, the both of them crashing to the floor. 'For heaven's sake, Seabourne, leave them where they are. Let's get on with the service.' I was only too relieved to accept this instruction from the exasperated old man.

It was a subdued preacher who ascended the pulpit for

his sermon. He was even more subdued when he discovered there was no Bible on the pulpit lectern. It would have been no inconvenience to the majority of preachers who have written their sermons with their text adorning the beginning. To someone who prided himself on his ability to preach extempore, it was disastrous.

I had intended to preach on verse 18 of the first chapter of the Gospel according to St Matthew, 'Now the birth of Jesus Christ was on this wise. When as his mother Mary was espoused to Joseph before they came together, she was found with child of the Holy Ghost.'

When the hymn before the sermon ended, I found myself looking at the congregation with a mind which had become blank. I managed to stammer the usual invocation, 'In the name of the Father and of the Son and of the Holy Ghost, Amen.' The congregation subsided into their seats and waited for the peroration. I stared at them in silence, vaguely trying to remember the text. They stared back. The sweat which had besprinkled my brow and drenched my shirt returned in even more copious quantities.

On my way to Pentwyn in my old Morris Minor I had imagined myself rising to great heights of pulpit oratory, destroying the Victorian image of the Blessed Virgin Mary as a mature matron and calling for sympathy for schoolgirl mothers. On my way back I mused on my mumbled *mélange* of pious platitudes which masqueraded as a sermon.

'Well, Bishop,' enquired my wife on my return home, 'how did it go?'

'I don't think I shall be asked to preach at another Mothers' Union deanery service.'

'What a relief for you,' she replied.

I made my way up the hill to Ashburnham Close the
following evening. I was undecided which of the two
houses I had to visit should be the first. Neither prospect
was pleasing. I was positive that my attempts to persuade
the Nicholls household to share their television viewing
with a contingent of Pontywen churchgoers would meet
with a frosty response. On the other hand I feared an
equally frosty attitude from the parents of Margaret
Price, who would regard my visit as an embarrassing
intrusion into their family affairs. The choice was decided
for me as I entered Ashburnham Close. Ernest Nicholls
was taking his Alsatian for its evening exercise. 'Hello,
Vicar,' he said. 'What brings you to this neck of the
woods?' He was a short bespectacled gentleman whose
stature made it difficult to determine whether it was he
or the dog who was in charge, especially since the hound
was dragging its owner along the pavement.

'As a matter of fact, Mr Nicholls,' I replied, 'I have
come to see you and Mrs Nicholls, amongst others.'

'In that case, we had better delay Bruno's trial of
strength for a short while and return to the "Hawthorns".' I was interested to see who would be the
winner in the tug of war that would follow. It was no
contest. One sharp word of command from the little man
and Bruno came to heel instantly. He was truly a man of
authority.

A brand new Rolls Royce with a personalised number plate, ENI, stood in the drive of the mock Tudor house, a product of the late thirties. The immaculately manicured lawn was bordered by rose trees already in full bud, evidently out-of-bounds territory for Bruno. 'Would you mind waiting a moment while I incarcerate the hound? My wife and daughter are out,' he said.

Man and beast disappeared round the side of the house while I surveyed the Price residence which stood opposite, built in the same black-and-white timbered style. Ashburnham Close had six such temples of opulence completed by a speculative builder in the nick of time before Hitler put paid to any further enterprise on his part. I wondered why someone like Margaret could have given herself to a young man so devoid of charisma as Mike. I remembered a saying of Mrs Richards, my landlady when I first came to Pontywen: 'Life is full of liquorice all sorts, isn't it?'

My musings were terminated abruptly by an invitation from Mr Nicholls to enter his domain. He produced an impressive bunch of keys and unerringly selected the one for his front door in a trice. I was ushered into the drawing room, and waved into a spacious armchair. 'May I offer you a drink, Vicar?' he asked.

'You may indeed,' I replied with alacrity.

'Scotch or a G and T?'

'Scotch, please, with just a touch of water.'

'In that case, I suggest you do the touching yourself. I prefer mine intact, or as W.C. Fields would say, untouched by human hand.' This he said with a pathetic attempt at mimicry. He went to the well stocked drinks cabinet and brought out a decanter three quarters full of whisky. The decanter and the glasses were of expensive cut glass, unlike the Vicarage set which were purchased from Roberts the Ironmonger, who was getting rid of pre-war stock.

Once he had settled into the armchair opposite me, he enquired the reason for my visit. I thought it better to launch into the deep immediately since the ladies of the house were not present. In one corner of the room, facing me, was a large television set enclosed in a walnut wood cabinet. I pointed at it and said, 'It's to do with that.'

He looked at me quizzically. 'What about that, Vicar? I can assure you that I have a licence for it. It's for my wife's pleasure more than mine. I am more interested in tinkering around with cars than with sitting passively to fill up my spare time.'

'I expect you will be sitting passively on 2 June, Mr Nicholls,' I replied, 'in common with all those who have a television set. However, I have come to you on behalf of those in the congregation at the parish church who are not fortunate enough to have the chance to see the coronation.'

He stared at me. 'What are you trying to say, dear man? That I should give it away to the poor and needy of the parish.'

'Of course not. I shall be having a television set in a week or so, courtesy of my brother, and I expect one or two others in the congregation will have one in time for the great day. My concern is that as many as possible will be able to see the service in Westminster Abbey. The only way that could happen would be if those who have sets would share their good fortune with others. I am going to invite as many people as I can into the Vicarage to view the proceedings. I am hoping that Mr Vaughan-Jenkins will do likewise in his place. I hope you do not think it an impertinence but I was wondering if you were prepared to do something similar.' There was a silence, as he removed his spectacles and wiped them in his handkerchief after breathing on them. I waited for him to put them back and look at me. There was an encouraging twinkle in his eyes when they focused on me.

'Well, Vicar, I must say that this is an unusual request but I do not think it an impertinence. However, my wife might think so. As far as I am concerned, I would be willing to invite a few people from your members to come and join us. For all I know Mrs Nicholls may be thinking to invite some of her friends along who have no set. All I can do is to have a word with her about this. She and my daughter have gone to Cardiff for the day and I shall be picking them up from the station later this evening. I shall give you a ring sometime during the next few days and let you know the verdict.'

We spent the next half hour talking about the state of Welsh rugby and the shortcomings of the Town Council. After the second tumbler of whisky, I left the 'Hawthorns' in a semi-alcoholic haze and prepared to make my way across the road to meet the parents of the pregnant young lady who had appeared on my doorstep two days previously.

The Price residence was showing signs of wear and tear on its exterior. The black paint had began to part company with the timber and the white plastered walls were several shades darker than their original colour, thanks to the polluted air of Pontywen. Weeds were fighting a winning battle with the gravel on the drive. The lawn was still awaiting its first cut and the flower border its replanting. I could imagine Mrs Nicholls making disparaging remarks about the eyesore opposite.

I searched in my pocket for a packet of Polo mints which I had bought providentially and wondered whether they would be sufficient to conceal the whisky aroma. As I stood at the gate, I recalled an incident at a wedding when the best man put a polo mint on my copy of the marriage service instead of the ring for which I had asked. The momentary giggle I enjoyed at the thought disappeared as I contemplated the interview which was about to take place. I walked up the drive slowly and stopped outside the porch, crunching a mouthful of mints before I felt ready to press the button of the doorbell. I swallowed the breath fresheners and announced my presence with a loud ring which echoed around the hall. A long silence ensued. I was about to write a message on the back of one of my visiting cards when I heard footsteps approaching on the gravel behind me. I turned to see a tall, well-built, grey-haired man and his wife, a short thin lady who was beside him. She was an older version of Margaret with the same brilliant blue eyes.

'Good evening, Vicar,' said Mr Price. 'Margaret has told us you would be calling some time this week.' His face was grim. He opened the door and invited me in. Mrs Price had not said a word but gave the impression that she was timid, fearful, very much subservient to her husband. They were both wearing light raincoats and wellington boots. 'If you will excuse us, we had better discard our walking apparel. Go into the drawing room, please, and make yourself comfortable. Would you care for a cup of tea. I am afraid we haven't anything stronger to offer you.'

'A cup of tea will be most acceptable, thank you,' I replied, still feeling the effect of something stronger. 'Milk and sugar?' enquired Mrs Price. Her voice and her tone were deferential. I was beginning to feel sorry for her.

'No milk and two spoonfuls of sugar, if you can spare it, that is.'

'That's all right, Vicar. We have plenty of sugar.' She disappeared into the kitchen in a flash, as if she was glad to escape. I wondered if she would still be in the kitchen when the time came for a discussion about her daughter's predicament.

As I waited for the tea to arrive I surveyed the contents of the 'drawing room'. A grand piano took up the space in the window. It was a Bechstein, but apparently neglected, by the amount of dust on its surface and the absence of any music copy. The piano stool stood some distance away, alongside the armchair on which I was seated, and served as a stand for a photograph of Mr and Mrs Price and their daughter ensconced in deckchairs at the seaside. The golden letters of the maker's name looked reproachfully from under the upturned lid of the piano.

The rest of the furniture and the pictures on the walls were not in the same exalted category. The three-piece suite was covered in moquette which had seen better days whilst the framed paintings were reproductions which could be seen in any store. There was an occasional table against the wall by the fireplace where the mantelpiece was the repository for two Spanish dancers captured in china and two framed wedding photographs. 'Change and decay in all around, I see,' I said to myself.

Suddenly Mr Price appeared in the doorway, relaxed in a knitted cardigan over an open-necked shirt and grey flannels, his feet reposed in tartan-coloured slippers. He carried a pipe and a tin of tobacco, evidently determined to be at ease. 'I hope you don't mind me smoking,' he said. 'It helps me to unwind at the end of the day. I suppose it is a hangover from babyhood. Then it was a dummy, now it's a pipe. Do you smoke, Vicar?'

'No, Mr Price. I once tried it in college when a friend suggested that cigarette smoke might ease the toothache from which I was suffering. Draw in some smoke and keep it inside your closed mouth, he instructed. My mouth was not closed for long, I began to cough violently. The toothache was worse than ever. It was an experiment which put me off tobacco for good.'

He attempted a smile which died almost as soon as it was born. By the lines on his face it would appear that Mr Price was not of a humorous disposition.

Any further discussion was delayed by the appearance of Mrs Price with tea for two on a tray decorated with a lace-edged cloth. As I thought, the Margaret problem was to be the subject of a *tête-à-tête* between her father and myself. After serving the tea, the lady of the house went back to the kitchen, leaving the two of us to sort things out.

'Well now,' began the master of the house, 'I gather from my daughter that she has come to you to put in banns of marriage. As I am sure you are aware, Vicar, she is under the age of consent. No way am I going to allow her to marry this young layabout who has not the means to support her. She is an intelligent, gifted child. You see that piano. Up until six months or so ago, she would be playing it like a concert artiste. Her piano teacher said that she had the ability to go far. That is why we sacrificed a lot of our money to buy that grand piano. Look at it now. It's a white elephant. Why in God's name should she throw all that away for somebody whose idea of music is a gramophone record of Frank Sinatra and who is quite content to live with her in one room in his parents' miner's cottage.'

All the time he was speaking, the tone and volume of his voice was rising and finished in a crescendo with the words 'miner's cottage'. My head was still spinning as a consequence of Mr Nicholls' hospitality. I strove to find words which could stem the tide of his anger and direct the conversation into a more rational channel. It was a vain exercise. My mind was blank. I sat looking at this man's despair at what he felt the fates had dealt to him and wondered how I could bring God into the impasse. Now I felt as sorry for him as I had felt for his wife earlier on. I had to break the silence.

'Mr Price, I realise how you must feel. May I ask, is Margaret your only child?'

He raised his head. 'We had a son who was run over by a baker's van which was speeding along when he was crossing the road. He was seven years of age. Robin was our first child, Margaret was born three years later. So, yes, she is our only child. All our love and affection was lavished on her. Whatever she wanted we gave her. Until we came to Pontywen she went to a private school in Cardiff, by which time our money was running out. I had lost my job as manager of an insurance company and am now working for a property developer in Newport at a much reduced salary. Life is hard enough without this disaster looming in front of us. I just cannot understand what she is doing.'

'I suppose there is very little logic in the thinking of an adolescent,' I replied. 'There is always that element of rebellion against what their elders expect of them. Please don't misunderstand me, but it may be that you set your sights on a target for her which she found too demanding, too intimidating. As a result she sought consolation in a love affair with a handsome young man whose intellectual gifts were few but whose physical attractions compensated for his lack of academic ability.'

He looked me in the eyes. 'You may be right, Vicar, but that is no answer to the question facing us right now. She was only a few months over the age of consent when the baby was conceived – a mere child. Under no circumstances whatsoever shall I give permission for the marriage. Her mother and I have told her that the best thing she can do is to go to the Moral Welfare home in Cardiff to have her baby. Then she can have it adopted and take up her life without the burden of caring for a child at her age. She had seven O levels last year and is in the lower sixth form at Pontywen Grammar School. Not only that, she has passed all her piano exams with top-level marks and was studying for grade seven when she threw it all up. It's a tragedy, Vicar, that is what it is. There she is, still out at this time of night. I expect she won't be in until ten at the earliest, when she'll go straight to bed.'

The head of the house was on the verge of tears as his voice began to break. He coughed and blew his nose.

'Mr Price,' I said, 'would you like me to have a word with Miss Lloyd Jenkins, the Moral Welfare organiser, before I see the young couple on Friday evening? She is a very kind, middle-aged lady with great experience in this field. When is the baby due?'

'The doctor says she is six months pregnant. As you can see by her size it looks like nine months. Her mother was the same when she was bearing our children. Yes, I would be very grateful if you could use your influence to get Margaret into the maternity ward at that place.'

'I shall do what I can, Mr Price. What's more important at the moment I shall try and persuade Margaret to see sense when she comes to the Vicarage. From what I can gather from her when she came to see me, that is not going to be easy. As you know full well, she is a young lady with a very strong will indeed. Anyway, I shall do what I can.'

He escorted me to the door without bothering to let his wife know that I was leaving. 'Please thank Mrs Price for the tea and biscuits.' He grunted an unintelligible reply as he watched me go down the drive.

It was half past nine when I arrived home. My wife

was stretched out on the settee in the front room, apparently fast asleep. I kissed her gently on the cheek only to get an instant response. 'And where do you think you have been, Prince Charming? While you have been away, I have had to deal with two couples intent on signing their death warrant and most of all with a telephone call from your erstwhile colleague and pain in the neck supreme.'

'You don't mean Charles Wentworth-Baxter, by any chance?' I enquired.

'How did you guess,' she replied, with heavy irony. 'He will be here at ten o'clock tomorrow. He sounded as if he were in his usual distraught state.'

Charles had been a fellow curate with me in Pontywen and after that was my underling when I was appointed Vicar. He must have been the most incompetent cleric ever and was fortunate to be appointed to a living, admittedly the most remote and sparsely populated parish in the diocese, the ecclesiastical equivalent of Siberian exile.

Over breakfast next morning we speculated about the reason for his visit. He and his wife, Bronwen, a former nurse at Pontywen Hospital, were now the proud parents of four children whom they had begotten in the space of five years. As Eleanor said, 'They are living far too close to the rabbit warrens out there. Give them long enough and they will be responsible for half the population of the parish. I suppose there's nothing else to do in the wilderness.'

'Perhaps that is why he wants to see me,' I replied.

'What do you mean, Frederick? To find out what's causing this population explosion?'

'Of course not. After all, his wife was a nurse and knows the facts of life. As far as I can see they must want a large family. In that case he will need a bigger parish with a bigger income – though why he should come to me about that I don't know. He should go to the Bishop.'

'Knowing Charles,' said Eleanor, 'he would be coming to you to find out how to approach his holy highness. If you remember, when he was here he could never do anything without your guidance even to the extent about when he would clean his teeth.'

'Pray, don't exaggerate, woman. Whatever the purpose of his call, we shall soon know.'

Unusually for him, he arrived at ten o'clock precisely. 'It must be important,' observed my wife as his car came down the drive. He remained inside the car for at least a couple of minutes in deep contemplation. 'Yes, very important,' she added. He opened the door slowly and looked inside the interior as he got out, apparently loath to leave his pre-war Austin Big Seven. He closed the door gently and then, staring at the Vicarage doorsteps, languidly ascended them as if in some kind of hypnotic trance. 'Put him out of his misery, love, and open the door before he rings the bell,' said Eleanor. 'Otherwise he might be standing outside on the step for another five minutes.'

When I opened the door, he jumped back like a startled fawn. 'I was just about to ring the bell,' he said. 'You gave me quite a fright.'

'Sorry, Charles, that's the last thing I want to do,' I replied. 'Come on in – it's great to see you. Go into the study and take a pew. Eleanor's got some coffee ready, haven't you, dear?'

She had appeared behind me as I greeted him. 'Freshly

made and guaranteed to please all our customers. How are the children?' she asked.

'Fine and very noisy as usual when I left them,' he said in a flat tone of voice.

'And Bronwen?'

'She's fine too.' If anything his tone of voice was even flatter and devoid of enthusiasm.

After Eleanor had left us to drink our coffee in the privacy of my study, Charles launched into the purpose of his visit immediately. 'Fred, I can't stand the boredom of that parish any more. There is absolutely nothing to do for somebody like me. If I were a country man it would be different. I could keep a few sheep and cows like the Vicar of Aberpengwm or perhaps become an ecclesiastical market gardener; I don't know a turnip from a parsnip. As for shearing a sheep or milking a cow, I would be a disaster. I'm a square peg in a round hole.'

'You are certainly in a hole, the worse hole in the diocese,' I replied, 'but how to get out of it will not be easy with your track record. Let's face it, Charles, you hardly set the Thames on fire in Pontywen, did you? Have you had a word with the Bishop? There are no livings vacant at the moment but he might keep you in mind when a suitable one crops up. Quite a few of the incumbents at this end of the diocese are well past the retiring age.'

'To be honest, Fred, I have approached him a couple of times but on each occasion I have had a polite but dusty answer. The reason why I have come to see you this morning is to ask whether I could help out in Pontywen occasionally – with the Gilbert and Sullivan Society, for example, or if you are going to do another door-to-door visitation of the parish. Anything to get away from those endless fields and the vacant faces when I look down at them from the pulpit, not to mention the tuneless roaring which goes under the heading of hymn singing. If the Bishop knows that I am keen enough to drive down to a town parish to help in any way I can, maybe it will persuade him that I am desperate to move to a populated area. He can't say that I am neglecting my parish when I could visit the entire church congregation in the space of an afternoon.'

I had never seen Charles more animated. Evidently solitary confinement had inspired him far more than his five years in Pontywen had ever succeeded in doing.

'You amaze me,' I replied. 'There was I thinking that the sinecure of your rural backwater would be paradise for you and instead it turns out to be hell. Before accepting your offer of help in this parish there are one or two practical details to be decided. For example, who is going to pay for your petrol for these excursions to Pontywen? Do you intend staying for a couple of days a week? Furthermore don't forget that I now have an excellent curate in Emlyn Howells. How is he going to feel about a former curate appearing on the scene? All these things will have to be worked out, Charles. One other thing, you must ask the Bishop's permission before you embark on this experiment. I suggest you do that first. Then we can talk.'

'Does that mean you will agree that I can come if the Bishop allows it?' he asked eagerly.

'Let's get stage one over first, shall we? Phone him later today. It's better to do that than write to him.'

When he left the Vicarage he was a changed man. He

skipped down the steps and shot into his car, smiling broadly. Once inside, he wound down the window. 'See you soon,' he shouted, and then roared up the drive as fast as his old Austin could manage to take him with its clapped out engine and faulty silencer.

'Well?' said Eleanor, when I came into the hall. 'What transpired to cause such a transformation in the poor worm who crawled out of his limousine on arriving? What magic have you worked?'

'You won't believe this,' I replied.

'I can believe anything about Charles Wentworth-Baxter but, pray, carry on with your explanation, Frederick. I am all ears.'

'He wants to come back to Pontywen to help out in any way he can – with the Gilbert and Sullivan rehearsals, even with another door-to-door survey of the parish – anything to get away from his sojourn in the wilderness.'

'And you said yes? Fred, you must be mad. He is a walking disaster. He will be trouble, not a help.'

'I can't see his lordship giving him *carte blanche* to leave his parish, however small it is, to work somewhere else as a kind of therapeutic hobby. Even if he is given the episcopal blessing, the next hurdle will be the Parochial Church Council. Knowing Charles, they will be very reluctant to provide cash for his petrol and his hospitality.'

Ten minutes later my wife and I had gone our different ways, she to relieve David Andrews at the surgery and myself to visit the home of Michael John Roberts at 13 Balaclava Street. As I made my way through the four streets which lay between the Vicarage and the Roberts abode, it was interesting to see the effect of the Festival of Britain in 1951 on the doors and windows of some of the houses. There was an end to the uniform drab. Blues, reds and even yellows had replaced the obligatory brown of the pre-war years, in a rebellion against the stultifying austerity of the forties. The outside of number 13 Balaclava Street had its woodwork decorated in a daffodil yellow. I raised the black-painted knocker and gently announced my presence in case one or other of the male occupants had been working nights. The curtains of the front window were held to one side as the caller was investigated by a lady whose curling pins were swathed in a large scarf, tied in the manner of a female pirate. As soon as she saw me she disappeared so quickly that it might have been an illusion on my part. I waited for the door to open but waited in vain.

Determined to get an answer, I decided like John Peel in the hunting song to awaken the dead. I banged on the door so loudly that the neighbour appeared from number 14, thinking that it was she who was being summoned. 'Hello, Vicar,' she said. 'I thought it was our door. They are in. Perhaps they are round the back. I'll go and call them for you.'

There was no need. The next instant number 13 had opened its portals. 'I thought I heard some knocking,' mumbled the embarrassed vision of the front window. 'Come on in, Vicar, will you please? Excuse my hair, will you? I've only just washed it. My 'usband and me are going out to a special do at the Miners' Welfare tonight. They've got Tommy Cooper coming. Go in the front room, I'll be with you in a minute.'

I went into the front room, which was furnished with a newly purchased artificial leather suite still smelling of the store room from which it had been removed. On the freshly papered striped wallpaper three flying ducks were *en route* to the ceiling and in front of the immaculately black-leaded hearth lay an imitation Persian rug for which no self respecting native of that country would claim responsibility.

When the lady of the house appeared next, she had discarded the pinafore she wore at my first sight of her and was clad in a red jumper designed to show off the salient points of her upper anatomy complete with a navy blue skirt to match. Apart from her yellow scarf disfigured by the coils of hair erupting underneath, Mrs Roberts was dressed impeccably for a housewife in Balaclava Street.

'Now then, Vicar. I know what you have come about. It's about our Mike and Margaret, isn't it? Well, I've got a surprise for you. They've gone up to Gretna Green to get married.'

3

'Mike knew that you was coming here today, but told me to keep it a secret,' said Mrs Roberts. 'Margaret's parents don't know. They went off this morning earlier to catch the train from Cardiff. He said that perhaps they might 'ave to wait three weeks before they can get married. I told 'im what's going to 'appen about your job in the pit. The next thing is you'll be drafted into the army and where will you be then?'

She sat on the settee next to me, clutching and unclutching her hands but completely dry eyed. 'As far as I know,' I replied, 'I think the right to get married at the blacksmith's forge at Gretna Green was abolished years ago. In any case, where's the money coming from to keep them while they wait to get married. I am sure Margaret has nothing. I don't suppose Mike has plenty in his pocket.'

'Oh, I think 'e've saved up quite a bit; never been one to throw his money about. In any case I've told them that they can stay with us until the time comes when they will 'ave somewhere of their own to go to. I know what it's like. We was in two rooms for years after we was married until we got this 'ouse, and what a state it was in when we had it. It took us ages to make it really fit to live in. Now, as you can see, it's beautifully furnished and painted.'

'Yes, it is, Mrs Roberts, a tribute to you and your

husband. Coming back to the purpose of my visit, I think I had better see Mr Fitzgerald the Diocesan Registrar. He will be able to tell me whether they can get married without parental consent. After that I feel I must see Mr and Mrs Price to let them know what has happened, whether Mike wants it kept a secret or not. They have a right to know, don't you agree?'

Her face turned the same colour as her jumper, a deep red. 'I suppose so,' she mumbled. 'Mind, if they had treated Margaret better and not wanted to put 'er in that Welfare 'Ome, this wouldn't 'ave 'appened.'

'I shall let you know what Mr Fitzgerald says and I shouldn't be surprised if Mr and Mrs Price come to see you once I have told them about the elopement. They will want to find out as much as they can. After all, she is their only child.'

I stood up and moved towards the door. She remained seated, her head bowed as if suddenly aware for the first time of the gravity of the situation as far as the Prices were concerned.

'Well, I'll be off now, Mrs Roberts,' I said. I moved into the passage which had been freshly papered with a covering of large red and white roses on a black background providing a lurid contrast to the daffodil yellow of the front door. She came quickly out of the front room and pushed past me to open the door into the street.

'Thank you for coming, Vicar,' she said, her eyes brimming with tears. 'I 'ope everything is going to be all right.'

Daniel Fitzgerald was a large, red-faced gentleman whose owlish countenance was decorated with a pair of horn rimmed spectacles. He seemed to spend far more time polishing them than wearing them. His favourite neckwear was a bow tie. A different one appeared each day in a wide variety of colours. His suit never changed, a shiny black serge which grew shinier as the years went by.

Like his suit, his opinions never changed. He was the ultimate diehard. For example, although he was the Diocesan Registrar in a Church in Wales diocese, he never ceased to mourn the passing of the Established Church or the Ecclesia Anglicana, as he called it, from its Welsh territory. There was one occasion when a highly respected Bardic lay reader was giving an address on St David at a lunchtime service in a town church. Daniel was sitting at the back, his arms spread out along the top of his pew. 'The Church in Wales is much older than the Church of England,' said the lay reader. This provoked a noisy banging on the pew with some kind of coin. Encouraged by this reaction the Bard asserted that while St David and the Welsh Saints had established Christianity throughout Wales the heathen English had to wait another century or so to be converted by Rome. By now Mr Fitzgerald was on his feet shouting, 'Nonsense. Don't listen to the man. He's talking balderdash.' Deciding that discretion was the better part of valour, the preacher left the pulpit only to be confronted in the Vestry at the end of the service by the irate Registrar.

The Diocesan Registry cum solicitor's office was in a street near the Cathedral. It was on the first floor of an Edwardian building, the ground floor of which was occupied by a gents' tailor. I went up the rickety stairs, then along the landing to the glass door bearing the name of Daniel T. Fitzgerald, LLB, SOLICITOR, DIOCESAN

REGISTRAR. I tapped gently on the door when a burst of typewriter activity had ended. 'Come in,' barked a contralto voice. The Amazon was seated behind a desk which was dominated by a large, ancient typewriter, probably a vintage model. Miss Muxworthy, bespectacled like her employer, had been in charge of the office since the First World War. I had come to know that her bark was worse than her bite.

'Ah, Vicar,' she said, in a much more friendly tone of voice. 'Mr Fitzgerald is expecting you. Take a seat while I tell him you are here. I think he is on the phone at the moment.' The seat was a leather-covered dining chair which like everything else in the office was showing signs of old age. The secretary was as tall and as large as her boss. On my first acquaintance with her as an ordinand, she towered above my five feet seven inches and so intimidated me that I began to stammer. Now we were the best of friends whenever I came to the office.

She disappeared into the next room and I could hear a conversation going on behind the closed door. As soon as it ended Miss Muxworthy reappeared and informed me that Mr Fitzgerald was now ready to receive me. I was greeted with a beaming smile from the registrar who came forward to shake my hand. 'Good to see you, Vicar,' he boomed. 'And how's your delightful lady wife? Still doctoring, I expect.'

Eleanor held a high place in his esteem ever since she had saved him from choking in a restaurant. It was during my curate days when we were celebrating her promotion to partnership in the practice by a rare night out at the Valley's only luxury dining place. We were seated at a table not far from where he was dining alone and enjoying his chicken supreme when a bone became lodged in his throat. His face had turned purple and he was gasping for breath. She was at his side in an instant and extracted the obstruction in a trice. Ever since that day we were remembered every Christmas with a bottle of best claret and a bouquet.

'Now then, what can I do for you?' he enquired, after asking about our two children and ushering me into another of his dining chairs. He sat back in the chair behind his desk and peered at me through his large spectacles, like a judge focusing his attention on someone in the witness box.

'I should like your advice on an urgent matter concerning some parishioners of mine,' I replied. He took off his spectacles, breathed on them and began to polish them with his handkerchief. 'Carry on, Vicar,' he said.

'Well, without going into too much detail, it appears that a young lady of seventeen who is pregnant and her young man who is nineteen have run off to Gretna Green to get married. The girl's parents have refused to give consent to her marriage in my church. Not only that, at the moment, they do not know she has eloped. My information has come from the young man's mother who lives in a small terraced house and who is prepared to let the couple have a room in which to begin their married life. The girl's parents live in a large detached house in the posh part of my parish. So what I should like to know from you, Mr Fitzgerald, is whether the blacksmith at Gretna Green can perform the ceremony. I have understood that such a marriage is no longer allowed to take place. Am I correct in thinking so?'

Once again he polished his spectacles and then proceeded to put them on again as if they were necessary to make a legal pronouncement.

'You are indeed correct, Vicar. The Marriage Act (Scotland) 1939 ended the blacksmith's shop weddings at Gretna Green. However, if they reside for fifteen days over the border after giving notice to a registrar and no one has objected, they will get away with the wedding. According to the 1949 Marriage Act, such a marriage would be lawful. I would imagine they would very soon find that out and find a district where they can reside and get a licence, that is, if they have the money to do it.' He took off his glasses to indicate that the official business was over.

'Apparently, according to the mother of the young man, who is a miner in Pontywen Colliery, he has saved a fair amount of money. So I think they should be able to support themselves for the fifteen days or so. Now I have the unenviable obligation of telling the girl's parents of the elopement. She has had the benefit of a private school education until her father's demotion brought her to Pontywen and to a state school. Margaret is an intelligent and gifted child with a possible career in music. Mike, her young man, has only his good looks to offer and very little besides.'

'All I can say, Vicar,' replied Mr Fitzgerald examining his spectacles minutely before replacing them, 'is that you have a very difficult pastoral problem. It is not for you to resolve it. You must stay on the sidelines and let the main protagonists sort it out. I agree that you must let the young lady's parents know immediately what is happening. After that it is up to them to decide what to do, whether they want to go chasing up to Scotland to find her or just accept the marriage as a *fait accompli* in a fortnight or so's time. It is up to them. You have done your part by providing the necessary information.'

An hour later I was pressing the button of the Prices' doorbell in Ashburnham Close. It was half past one. I had to ring twice before I had an answer. A flustered Mrs Price opened the door, wearing an apron. 'You must excuse my dress, Vicar. I have been preparing the food for dinner this evening. We have company coming. Do come in, will you? I expect you have news for us after seeing Mike's parents.'

She led me into the lounge and enquired if I would like a cup of tea or coffee. 'No, thank you,' I replied. 'I shan't stop long. I am afraid I have news for you which you will find disturbing. Mike and Margaret have eloped. They have gone to Gretna Green to get married. I have consulted the Diocesan Registrar and he informs me that although the blacksmith's shop is no longer available for weddings, they can get married by residing for a minimum of fifteen days anywhere in Scotland. I only found out earlier this morning from Mike's mother and went immediately to the Registrar to discover what the legal position was.'

Mrs Price's face drained of colour and her bottom lip began to quiver. She collapsed into an armchair. 'I must phone her father straight away. He will be furious. He worships that child. He thinks she is the most wonderful creature on God's earth. It's almost an obsession with him, Vicar. We paid out money for her to go to the private school in Cardiff. We couldn't really afford it but he insisted that she wasn't going to any Valley school. Then we paid out money on that grand piano when there wasn't much in the bank. On top of all that he lost his well-paid job and we had to come down here to a Valley school for her. This will kill him.'

She began to shed tears. In no time at all she was sobbing violently. I went to her and put my arm around her. 'How am I going to tell him?' she wailed. 'He will be so angry, so very angry.' It was obvious that she was in fear of him and his reaction to the news when it was told him.

'Would it be any help,' I said quietly, 'if I phoned him and told him what has happened? It will save you all the aggravation. I shall try to be as diplomatic as I can in letting him know.'

Her convulsive sobbing began to subside. 'I should be most grateful if you would do that,' she replied. 'You don't know how uncontrollable he can be in certain circumstances. You can phone him from here if you like. The sooner he is told the better.'

'I think it would be wiser if I spoke to him from the Vicarage,' I replied. 'It won't take me two minutes to get there. I have the car outside.' I had no intention of talking to the irate Mr Price, with his wife hovering around me. There was also the extra time it would give me to think of the right approach.

She gave me his office telephone number. 'Ask for extension 7,' she said. 'He should be back from lunch by now.'

During the short space of time it took me to drive back to the Vicarage I rehearsed several opening gambits, from 'Mr Price, your daughter has eloped' to an enquiry after his health followed by a gradual imparting of the news in a couple of stages. The net result of this exercise was mental turmoil when I lifted the phone to dial the office number. As I did so, Eleanor's head appeared round the door of the study.

'Where on earth have you been, Fred? Your lunch was ready ages ago. I couldn't wait for you any longer. I have to go to the Maternity Clinic now. You will find your shepherd's pie in a somewhat dried-up condition in the oven. The children are out with Marlene. Next time, phone me, there's a good boy, if you are going to be late for your lunch. See you later.'

Before I could reply she had gone through the front door. By the time I had dialled the Price number, I could hear her car speeding up the drive. I wished I could have had a word with her before making my call.

Extension 7 was engaged. I had to wait several minutes before it was free. While I waited I remembered the words of Daniel Fitzgerald. 'You must stay on the sidelines.' Here I was in the middle of the pitch. My head was in a whirl and my heart was pounding. 'Hello!' said the voice curtly.

'Is that Mr Price?' I asked feebly, knowing full well that it was he.

'Yes, what can I do for you?' There was as much warmth in his tone as you would get from a lighted match in a freeze-up.

'This is the Vicar, Mr Price.'

'I am sorry, Vicar, I didn't recognise your voice. How did you get my number?' Evidently he did not like to be phoned at the office.

'I had it from Mrs Price. You see, I have urgent news for you. It's about Margaret.'

There was a momentary silence at the other end. 'Don't tell me something has happened to her.' He sounded like a different man, panic-stricken, a disinte-grated iceberg.

'Nothing has happened to her like an accident, for example. However, I am afraid that she and Mike have eloped to Gretna Green.'

'What!' he bellowed, blasting my eardrums.

'Apparently they went off early this morning, expecting to get married in the blacksmith's forge. They will find that it is no longer a marriage venue. However, I under-stand that if they reside in a district across the border for fifteen days they will be able to get married. I have been to see the Diocesan Registrar and he assures me that this is the case.'

From the amount of heavy breathing at the other end which accompanied my report on the elopement, I began to fear that he was on the verge of an imminent heart attack. The heavy breathing continued when I had fin-ished speaking. It was obvious that he was incapable of speech, either through incoherent rage or a dangerous medical condition.

'Mr Price,' I said, 'are you there?' There was no reply. 'Mr Price,' I shouted. I heard a muffled noise and then followed a complete silence. I put down the receiver and dialled the office number.

I dialled three times. Each time the line was dead. After a frantic third attempt to contact the office, I realised that I was attempting the impossible. Since the receiver was dangling at the extension 7 end, the phone at the Vicarage was unable to contact the office number.

I put the receiver down and tried to think of the nearest place with a phone. There was a telephone kiosk in the town square but there was always someone in there, with one or two people waiting outside. The thought of the town square reminded me of Howells the greengrocers. Moelwyn and Myfanwy Howells had a phone which Charles Wentworth-Baxter used to call me when he was a lodger there. I ran out to the car and drove off at high speed. There was a parking place outside the shop. I pulled up with a screech of tyres, jumped out of the car, and dashed into the shop to the amazement of three old ladies who were having a gossip on the pavement.

'You're in a hurry, Vicar,' said Moelwyn, who was weighing some tomatoes for a customer.

'May I use your phone?' I gasped. 'It's urgent.'

'I can see that,' he replied. 'You know where it is – on the window ledge in the living room.' *En route* I collided with Myfanwy, who was coming to help in the shop.

'What on earth is the matter, Vicar?' she enquired.

'It's a matter of life and death. I've got to get to the phone. I'll explain later.'

'Oh dear,' she exclaimed.

When I got to the phone, I realised I had not brought the piece of paper with the office number on it.

'Myfanwy!' I shouted. 'Where is the telephone directory?' She came running into the room with the directory.

'Sorry,' she said. 'I took it into the shop this morning to look up a number and forgot to put it back.'

As I thumbed through the pages devoted to the name Morris, my frustration became intense. Every second wasted in finding the number was adding to the possibility that by the time the extension 7 office was reached, it would be too late. At last I discovered W.G. Morris & Co. at the bottom of the column.

'Morris and Company, can I help you?' said the receptionist.

'This is urgent,' I replied. 'Can you get somebody to go to Mr John Price's office at once. I am afraid that he must have been taken ill. He seems to have dropped the receiver and I cannot get any response from him. I am his Vicar and I had to give him some news which might have come as too great a shock for him. Will you please let me know what has happened? This is Pontywen 279.'

While I waited for a reply, I told Myfanwy what had happened.

'I could see by your face that something drastic was going on. Your face is as white as a sheet. I'll get you something to bring the colour back to your cheeks.' She went out and came back with a tumbler of whisky.

The minutes stretched into an eternity.

Then the phone rang. I picked it up, my hands shaking. 'Mr Morris wants to speak to you,' announced the shaky voice of the receptionist.

'I am afraid, Vicar,' said the property developer, 'that I have some bad news for you. John Price has suffered a massive heart attack. The ambulance has just taken him away for examination at the hospital but the expectation is that he will not be able to survive. I wonder if you would be so good as to break the news to Mrs Price. It would be much better coming from you rather than from his place of employment.'

As I drove to Raglan House in Ashburnham Close, I wondered if I had been wise to offer my services to Mrs Price as the herald of bad tidings. Perhaps if she had told her husband, it might have softened the blow somewhat. Now I had to be the bearer of even worse news to a lady who appeared to be frightened of her own shadow. Small wonder I kept crashing my gears.

For the third time in two days I made my way up the drive in trepidation, wondering why on earth I had got myself involved with the young couple instead of sending them away when it was apparent that I could not marry them. There was an instant response when I rang the door bell. Evidently, Mrs Price must have been hovering around the hall waiting for the call from her husband once he had been informed about the runaways.

She was startled to see me. 'Vicar, I didn't expect to see you so soon again. Come in, please. I haven't heard from my husband as yet.'

I waited to speak until we were both seated in the front room. She had been studying my face ever since I had appeared at the door, and I felt that she had a premonition of what I was about to tell her.

'I am afraid I have some bad news for you. Your husband has had a very bad heart attack and has been taken to hospital in Newport. They are going to carry out an examination, of course, but apparently it is extremely serious. I am so sorry to have to be such a merchant of gloom.' I went to her and put my arm round her shoulder. She looked shrivelled up by all that had happened in such a short time to her daughter and now to her husband.

To my amazement she put aside my arm and stood up. 'We must get an SOS message on the wireless to Margaret at once. She means a lot more to him than I do. I was afraid that something like this would happen. How do we do that?'

'I should think that we should have to inform the

police and ask them if it is possible to have it broadcast, or perhaps the hospital can do it. In any case they don't broadcast an SOS until just before they read the news at six o'clock. So there's plenty of time. Would you like me to drive you to the hospital first of all? Then we can ask there how to go about it. More important than that, you will be able to be at your husband's bedside at this critical time in his life. He will need you now more than ever.'

'Vicar,' she replied. 'He has never needed me, apart from supplying him with meals and clean clothes. I doubt if it will make much difference whether I am at his bedside or not. It would be much more comfort to him if Margaret was there. That is why it is so important to try to get her to come back. If anybody could rally him, she could.'

Soon we were on our way to the hospital. The traffic on the Valley roads was very heavy and it took us an hour and a half to get to the hospital. Throughout the journey Mrs Price was completely composed and spoke of her early married life with her husband and how happy it was until Robin her son was killed in an accident.

The hospital car park was full. I took the liberty of parking in one of the places reserved for the consultants. At the information office there was a long queue which we ignored and went to the Matron's office. A cleric's collar is always an open sesame in a hospital and in no time at all we were at the bedside of the unconscious John Price. A consultant, a junior doctor and the nurses were in attendance in the side ward to which he had been taken. 'I am afraid that your husband has had a massive heart attack,' said the consultant. 'He has been X-rayed and it has revealed that his heart is in a very bad state. This collapse could have happened at any time. I am sorry to say that there is nothing we can do for him. He could die today. He may last out a few more days at the most. It must be a great shock for you. If it is any consolation I can assure you that he has been living on borrowed time for a while.'

'Thank you for being so frank,' she replied. 'There is one thing. My daughter is somewhere in Scotland. She is our only child and my husband was very devoted to her. I wonder if it would be possible to send out an SOS for her on the wireless.'

'I should think so,' he said. 'I would suggest that you go to Matron's office. You can say that I have asked that the request should be made. She will then contact the police who will give the necessary information to the BBC.'

'Would you like me to go while you stay with your husband?' I said to her.

'That is very kind of you. By the way, doctor, this is our Vicar. He has been a great help over the past few days. You see, my daughter has eloped to Scotland.'

The consultant came to her and held her hand. 'My dear lady, you have really been through the mill, haven't you?' he murmured.

As I came to the Matron's office door she was advancing towards me from the opposite direction. A tall buxom lady with a military bearing, she was an imposing figure, authority personified. 'Can I help you, Vicar?' she demanded, rather than asked. I felt glad that I was not the hospital chaplain.

'It is rather urgent, Matron. I wonder if I could have a few words with you in the privacy of your office.'

She gave me the kind of look which Mr Bumble would have given to David Copperfield when he asked for a second helping.

'I am afraid it will have to be a few because we are very busy this afternoon. Come on in, will you?'

We went past the secretary at her desk and into the inner sanctuary. 'Take a seat,' she ordered, while she stood towering over me in a most disconcerting fashion. Evidently my words had to be few.

'I have come from the Llewellyn ward where a parishioner of mine has been brought in with a massive heart attack. The consultant has asked me if you could inform the police to contact the BBC with an SOS message. He says that the patient is in imminent danger of death. His only child, a daughter, has eloped to Scotland and her whereabouts there are not known. I should think not very far across the border. By the way, she is six months pregnant.'

She sat down. Her whole attitude changed. 'I take it that the mother is here in the ward,' she said quietly.

'She is indeed. I offered my service as a courier so that she could stay by her husband's bedside.' The Matron produced a sheet of paper from a drawer in the desk. 'Shall we get the details, Vicar, and I shall be in touch with the police immediately.' When she had written the necessary information she stood up and escorted me to the door. 'Will you please tell Mrs Price that I shall be along to see her shortly,' she added as I left.

When I returned to the ward I found the curtains screening the bed. There was no sound of a conversation behind them. I hovered around for a few seconds. 'Mrs Price,' I whispered.

She appeared at once, still as dry-eyed and composed. 'They have gone for the time being,' she said. 'Are they going to send out an SOS for Margaret?'

'The Matron says that she will contact the police immediately. She expects that they will be able to get the message broadcast before the six o'clock news. She said that she will be along to see you soon.'

'Everybody is being very kind. It helps to restore your faith in human nature, I must say. I suppose it takes something like this to happen to make you realise that.'

It amazed me that the frightened wife who spoke the minimum when I first encountered her in the presence of her husband was the self-possessed lady who had chatted to me all the way to Newport, and who now appeared to be completely in charge of the situation. 'Do you want me to stay with you for a while, Mrs Price?' I asked.

'You must be a very busy man, Vicar. I am most grateful for all that you have done as it is. No, thank you. You get on your way. I have a sister in Cardiff. I shall give her a ring later on and let her know what has happened. She and her husband have a car. So they can be here in no time later today.'

'What about Mr Price? Has he any relatives? I can ring them if you want me to. It will be no trouble.'

She caught hold of my arm. 'That is very good of you but there is no need. His only brother died of a heart attack a few years ago. Apparently his father died in the same way. His mother died only recently. So there is no one on that side alive. I shall let you know what has happened and I shan't forget your kindness. Would you like to see him before you go?' She parted the curtains.

There lay her husband, his eyes closed, his mouth wide open and minus his dentures. We stood for a moment in silence. 'How are the mighty fallen,' she said.

4

No sooner had I arrived in the Vicarage than the telephone made its presence felt. 'Not again!' expostulated my wife. 'That's the third time in the last ten minutes.' As I picked up the receiver she added, 'And you have a lot of explaining to do for your playing away from home for the past three or four hours. Your children are beginning to think that they are fatherless.'

I put my hand over the mouth of the receiver. 'Be patient, my sweet, and all will be revealed.'

'Ernest Nicholls here,' announced the voice at the other end. 'I have had a word with my wife about sharing our television set with some of the parishioners. You will be pleased to know that she says that we shall be able to entertain four of them but no more than that. Apparently she has already invited a few of her friends but in view of your plea that we should share our good fortune in having a set with those who have none she felt obliged to do something about it. Quite frankly, I am amazed that she has done so.' I was about to express my agreement but controlled myself and said how delighted I was at her generosity. I put the phone down and then put my arms around Eleanor who was standing at my side.

'Don't think you can get around me by doing that,' she said in mock anger. 'Come on, out with it, but before that, what was the call about?'

'That, my dear love, was Mr Nicholls informing me

that his good lady had consented to having four specially picked specimens of the Pontywen proletariat in her drawing room to watch the coronation. He informed me that he was amazed at this condescension.'

'And so say all of us,' exclaimed my wife. 'Now comes the problem of deciding what four persons of virtuous behaviour are to be selected for this great privilege. Perhaps it would be wise to put a number of names into a hat and make a lottery of it.'

'Do you know what,' I replied. 'I think that would be a very good idea. First prize see it with the Nicholls, second prize join Vaughan-Jenkins, third prize view at the Vicarage. Runners-up look through the shop window outside Jones the Wireless.'

'Well, at least we seem to be making some progress towards D-Day,' said Eleanor. 'Next, would you mind explaining your absence from the bosom of your family for most of today? You had better go and see your children after you have done so. They may have forgotten what you look like by now.'

'When you have heard what I have to say, I think you will agree that I have had a very busy and very taxing day.'

By the time I had recounted all that had happened she came to me and kissed me. 'My dear love,' she murmured, 'you have indeed had a very taxing day and evidently it is not over yet. It is not long before the six o'clock news. We must listen for the SOS. I shouldn't be surprised from what you have told me that you will have a call from the hospital to say that Mr Price has died. It will be a miracle if he survives until the time his daughter arrives, that is, of course, if she does arrive.'

There was no miracle. No sooner had we heard the SOS message on the wireless than there was a telephone call from the sister on the ward to say that Mr Price had died and that Mrs Price would like to see me. 'I don't get this,' I said to Eleanor. 'It's only just an hour or so ago that she told me that her sister would be coming to the hospital and that my services were no longer required for the time being. From what she said at her husband's bedside, she is hardly overwhelmed with grief. Strange woman!'

'You can say that again,' my wife replied. 'If I were you, I should not rush back down to Newport. Go and see the children and I'll get you something to eat. She has had more than her fair share of attention from you already.'

It was past eight o'clock when I entered the hospital. Mrs Price was waiting for me in the entrance hall. She smiled when she saw me. 'It is very good of you to come once again after all you have done for me today. I am sorry to have to impose on you once more. Apparently my sister is not at home. Matron advised me that it would be advisable for me to get back home as soon as possible and out of the hospital environment. You are the only one I could think of to take me back. I hope you don't mind, Vicar.' She spoke as if she were requesting a lift after a shopping expedition, not a bereavement.

All the way back to Pontywen she chatted incessantly about everything from the coronation to what needed to be done to the house and garden. She wondered if she would hear from Margaret later that evening and what her daughter's reaction to the news of his death would be. 'It would be wonderful if she gave up the idea of getting married and stayed with me instead, even if it means her bringing up her baby here.' The only time she mentioned her husband was confined to a single sentence almost at the beginning of our journey from the hospital. 'Well, all I can say is that I am glad John did not have to suffer and died without an atom of pain.' Then she went on to talk about making arrangements for the funeral and the refreshments to follow at the house. She hoped Margaret would be there to help with preparing the food. 'She's a good little cook, you know.'

'I suppose you will want to get back to the Vicarage now,' she said, as we stopped in the drive.

'If you don't mind,' I replied. 'But I will come in for a few minutes. Perhaps your sister will be home by now. I'll wait until you have phoned her. Maybe she will come over and stay the night with you.'

'Let me make you a cup of tea,' she said. 'Go into the sitting room and make yourself at home. Once I've put the kettle on I'll go and phone my sister again.' I went to the window and looked out at the overgrown grass on the lawn. Evidently John Price had thrown in the sponge. From the conversation in the car it appeared that Mrs Price was about to remedy the neglect which was apparent inside and outside the house. Far from being a cloud descending upon her, the death of her husband had lifted a cloud which had been hanging over her for many years. It was a time of release.

My musings were interrupted by the ringing of the telephone. There was the sound of hurried footsteps in the passage from the kitchen to the hall. 'Margaret,' exclaimed her mother and then burst into tears for only the second time that day. I came out from the sitting room to see if there was anything I could do. Mrs Price was standing holding the receiver and sobbing uncontrollably. I took the receiver from her hands gently.

'Mother!' repeated a tearful voice at the other end.

'Margaret, this is the Vicar. Your mother is too upset at the moment to speak.'

'How is my father, Vicar?' She sounded desperate. I took a deep breath.

'I am sorry to have to tell you this but he passed away a few hours ago.' She began to cry. I had never felt so helpless in my life, standing between two wailing women, the one in Pontywen and the other somewhere in Scotland. It was Margaret who was first to stifle her grief.

'Can I speak to my mother now, please?' she asked.

'Mrs Price,' I said firmly, 'Margaret wishes to speak to you now, otherwise her money will begin running out in the call box.' Mention of the call box seemed to bring her to her senses.

'I'll get her to reverse the call,' she said. I handed her the receiver and retreated rapidly into the lounge, closing the door behind me. I had no wish to be further involved in the three-way conversation.

Some ten minutes or so later the receiver was replaced and a somewhat shame-faced Mrs Price came into the sitting room. 'I am sorry about that, Vicar. I just couldn't help myself. Anyway the good news is that my daughter will catch the train home first thing in the morning. Even better than that, she says she will stay with me until she has the baby and then later on decide whether to get married or not. I have a feeling that she will not. I can look after the child if she wants to carry on with her education. It will give me a new interest to brighten up my life. What does that old hymn say, "God moves in a mysterious way, His wonders to perform"?' A contented smile spread across her tear-stained face. Evidently John Price had not died in vain.

She assured me that she was in no need of company that night and that she would phone her sister after I had gone. As I opened the door of my car to drive off, she said, 'That reminds me. I must get someone from John's office to bring his car back tomorrow. Perhaps I can get some driving lessons once this is all over and so can Margaret later on. It is pointless having a machine if you can't use it. It will be quite a challenge to be in the driving seat.'

The next morning I had a telephone call from the Bishop. 'Charles Wentworth-Baxter has rung me with a strange request. He wishes to leave his parish for a few days each week to come and assist you in Pontywen. I have told him that since you already have a most capable assistant in Emlyn Howells there is clearly no need of any extra help. In any case, with Wentworth-Baxter's record in your parish I should imagine he would be much more of a hindrance than a help. It is obvious to me that his request springs more from a desire to escape boredom than an eagerness to give of his best in a more populated parish. However, I have not forbidden him from coming but I have informed him that he must have your complete agreement and that this experiment must be for a limited time only, otherwise his parish will feel neglected.'

No sooner had I put the phone down than there was a ring on the doorbell. There was no mistaking that ring, which consisted of two short jabs on the push button followed by a long pressure which would awaken the dead. The above had arrived. Charles stood on the doorstep, grinning at me. 'Reporting for duty, sir,' he said and gave me a sloppy salute.

'There'll be no duty for you today, I can assure you,' I told him. 'There are a lot of things to be sorted out before you can set foot in Pontywen again. Come on in. I have just had the Bishop on the phone and he is not at all over the moon about your "strange request", as he called it. Still, never let it be said that I have stood in your way in your bid for advancement to greater things in the diocese. Go into the study while I make us a cup of coffee. Eleanor is at the surgery.'

The inane grin was still on his face when I came back with a tray of coffee and biscuits. I felt a strong urge to wipe it from his face as we sat sipping the hot coffee. I launched into the offensive. 'Charles,' I said, 'if you are going to come back here you will have to work ten times harder than previously. For example, Emlyn Howells is in the process of setting up a Scout troop in the parish. We shall need someone to inaugurate a Cub pack. That will be one of your first tasks.' The smile vanished and a frown took its place. He stared at me in disbelief. 'Then again, I am thinking of starting some kind of fellowship for the old-age pensioners on a Wednesday afternoon in the church hall. You know the kind of thing. Tea and biscuits, dominoes, whist drives and a sing-song. With your ability at the piano you would be the ideal person to get it off the ground.' The colour was beginning to drain from his face.

'The other project I have in mind is a young people's club with rock and roll records on an amplifier, table tennis tournaments, spelling bees and so on. If you want youngsters to be linked to the church this is one of the best ways. I have been thinking of forming a committee to organise it. You could have the job as chairman.'

By now he seemed to be on the verge of a nervous collapse. 'What about Emlyn Howells?' he stammered. 'Shouldn't he be doing these things? I was thinking I could help out with the Gilbert and Sullivan crowd and with doing some door-to-door visiting. I'll be no use at any of those projects you have mentioned, no use at all.'

'In that case, dear Charles, it is no use you coming to Pontywen at all. As it was in the beginning, is now and ever shall be as far as you are concerned. All you want to do is to escape from your noisy children and your too peaceful rural surroundings for a few days a week. It is not work that you want but an excuse to idle away your time in Pontywen rather than in your parish backwater. Sorry, my friend, but it is not on.'

He sat hunched up in the armchair, a picture of misery. I waited for his reply. There was a two-minute silence. Then to my amazement, he said, 'You are right. I know. I was never energetic in Pontywen. So how could you believe that I would be different if I came back? The truth is I am desperate. Things are chaotic in the house. Bronwen seems to have lost interest. It's like living in a pigsty. I go around in underclothes that have not seen a washtub for ages, not to mention my clerical shirt which is a permanent fixture. I never know when to expect my meals and when I do get them they are not very appetising to say the least. I tell you what, Fred, I am getting to the stage when I will not be able to put up with it any longer. It's as bad as that.'

'When you say that you will not be able to put up with

it any longer, Charles, does that mean you will start helping in the house. With all the time you have on your hands, why can't you do some washing? I am sure you will never be able to do any ironing but I am positive you could wash clothes, and napkins if it comes to that. As far as the meals are concerned, there is no reason why you couldn't do some cooking. From what I can see, it is poor Bronwen who is desperate, much more than you. With four children born within the space of five years I should think it would drive most women to distraction. For God's sake, Charles, stop thinking about yourself. Turn your attention to Bronwen and the children. Your responsibility is to them first and foremost.'

Suddenly the savaged sheep turned into a tiger. He stood up, his eyes blazing. 'And what gives you the right to talk like that?' he shouted. 'Since when did you do any washing or cooking. You've got it made, with an affluent wife who can pay people to do those menial tasks and look after your two children. I came to you because I thought you were the one person that could help me. I had forgotten how holier than thou you could be. I shan't impose on your precious time any longer. Don't bother to see me out.' He strode towards the door, which he flung open in a melodramatic fashion. The front door was closed with a slam that shook the house. That was followed by an equally violent slam of his car door. The starter motor was given similar treatment but it failed to arouse the engine. After a multiplicity of attempts, the battery refused to cooperate any further. A long silence reigned.

I looked out of the window to behold a pathetic figure

spreadeagled over the driving wheel, his nose almost in contact with the dashboard.

From his very first encounter with a steering wheel when he drove the Vicar's car into a ditch Charles had had no luck with cars. The episode in the ditch was his one and only driving lesson in the company of Father James Whittaker. Prior to his move into the wilds, which necessitated the use of a car, he had a course of lessons with Jones the Garage who had promised to supply him with a second-hand car at a reasonable price. At the end of the first twelve lessons, during which he had done irreparable harm to the gear box and had dented the car in several places, Elias Jones suggested that he should use a bicycle to get around his rural parish. Undaunted, Charles went to the driving school which had recently taken over the second-hand furniture shop in Pontywen.

After another twelve lessons the instructor at the 'Safe Drive' establishment decided that his pupil was ready to sit the first of several driving tests. To his amazement Charles was given a licence to drive. Eleanor suggested that his clerical collar must have convinced a gullible examiner that someone who worked for the Almighty would have supernatural power to avoid accidents no matter how incompetent he might be. Idris the Milk insisted that either the examiner had been bribed or he was drunk at the time of the test. Whatever the reason, Charles was now let loose in charge of a car for good or for ill.

The Austin Big Seven was the third car he had bought since he had become Vicar of Penglais. The first one he had was the result of an advertisement in *The Times*. 'Impecunious curate requires car for use in rural parish.

£100 maximum.' He had a reply from a Morris Minor enthusiast who offered a car which had been rebuilt. It was a 1932 Morris Minor. After six months in his new parish, he turned the wheel to enter his ramshackle garage. The wheel was turned to the left and the car went straight on into the wall which bordered the garage. The steering wheel had snapped. At least the Almighty had seen to it that the car was not on the road. Apparently the rod had been involved in an accident and had been rewelded. Since Charles had lost the letters from the vendor, there was nothing he could do to claim compensation.

His next venture was the acquisition of his late father's car. The Reverend Septimus Wentworth-Baxter had been elevated to a place prepared for him in the heavenly establishment as a loyal servant of the Church of England for fifty-two years since his ordination. As a result Charles had been able to fill some of the rooms in his large Vicarage with furniture appropriate to its age. In tune with the furniture was the aged Bentley which consumed more petrol than the twice-weekly bus visiting Penglais to take its inhabitants to market. Fortunately for Charles its engine decided to give up the ghost and join its former owner as no longer part of this mortal world.

So my ex-curate decided to come back to Pontywen to buy a used car from Elias Jones 'at a reasonable price'. It was a car which could be parked outside the Bishop's palace not at all looking out of place, according to the vendor. Since Charles was in urgent need to park his car in that vicinity he agreed to pay Elias £200 for the privilege, a sum which he could ill afford in view of his family commitments. After two breakdowns, at the second of which the family were stranded on top of a bare mountain inhabited by sheep and rarely by human beings, Charles accused Elias of malpractice. The garage owner accused his customer of abusing the machine he had purchased. It was deadlock, neither of the parties having the money or indeed the will to pursue the matter any further.

Now, Charles was faced with the situation of asking Elias Jones to come to his aid or of walking two miles to the next garage. Evidently the decision was one with which his brain was unable to cope. He was in limbo.

Since I was fully acquainted with this void which perpetually bedevilled my former curate, there was only one thing I could do. I went out and opened the car door. I shouted, 'Charles!' He sat up in an instant, like a schoolboy pinpointed by a tyrannical schoolmaster. 'Come on into the study and we'll phone Elias Jones to come and see to it,' I said.

'Over my dead body!' he snarled. 'In any case, it's nothing to do with you. I'll walk down to the Mile End Garage and ask them to come and see what is wrong. It may be Elias Jones's car but they will have a much better idea of what to do with it than he would. That man's a fraud, a twister.'

'Look, Charles,' I said, 'you can phone the Mile End from here. It will take you half an hour to walk there and then you'll have to wait for them to bring you back. I know you must be very upset but, for your own sake, calm down and try to get this car business sorted out. Otherwise you're going to get stranded in Pontywen.'

A few minutes later he was on the phone, pleading

with the proprietor of the 'Mile End' Garage to rescue him. The desperation in his voice was sufficient to bring an instant response. In no time at all a mechanic was attending to the stricken machine. As soon as he opened the bonnet, he exclaimed, 'Oh! My God!' which was followed by an apology for blasphemy in the presence of two men of God. 'When did you last have the car serviced?' he asked.

Charles could not remember. 'In fact,' he said, 'I only take it to the garage when something goes wrong.'

After a cursory examination the mechanic diagnosed a major malfunction which would require a day's work at the very least, that is, if the necessary spare parts were available. He produced a tow rope from the back of the van and 'affixed' it to the Austin Big Seven. 'Hop in, Vicar, and be careful steering. I'll drive slowly in any case, so don't worry.'

This did nothing to assure someone whose steering was suspect even when a tow rope was not involved and whose cup of woe had overflowed so much that he was unable to think straight, let alone drive straight.

'I don't wish to interfere, Charles,' I said, 'but would you like me to steer the car? I have had experience of doing it.' I did not add that it was only on one occasion, and that ended with me steering the Rural Dean's car into the gatepost at the entry to his drive. However, that was on a dark night with only the side-lights on, not in broad daylight, I told myself. Also, I was being towed by my wife and not by a car mechanic, an expert on towing.

He accepted my offer with alacrity. The panic-stricken look disappeared from his face only to be replaced by a furrowed brow as he contemplated the absence of his car for a day or two. 'How am I to get back to Penglais? What's more, how am I going to get down here to pick the car up. There isn't another bus from the village this week.'

'If our friend here will drive us back from the garage, I will run you home. When the car is ready, I will come to your place and drive you back to pick it up. How does that suit you?'

He put his arm round my shoulder. 'Thanks, Fred. You have been a real pal to me once again. I'm sorry for that outburst earlier on but things have really got on top of me. Perhaps something will turn up to change my luck, you never know.'

The journey to the garage was uneventful, unlike the news given by the garage owner. 'I am afraid you will have to pay for a new engine or a reconditioned one. When did you last put oil in this car? There isn't a drop left in it. Charles looked at him blankly. 'I have never put oil in it and I wouldn't know where to put it anyway.'

Ernest Williams, proprietor of the Mile End Garage, raised his eyes to heaven and then brought them down to focus on the cleric opposite him. 'Well, Reverend,' he said, 'I suppose you believe in miracles but even miracles won't work on cars that haven't got oil in them. If I were you, I would get cracking on learning how to look after a car or you'll be needing miracles to pay for a new engine every year.'

When we arrived at the Vicarage, Eleanor's car was parked outside the garage. 'You had better come in, Charles, and have something to drown your sorrows before I take you home. You look as if you need it badly.'

As we came through the front door, my wife came to meet us. 'What has been happening?' she asked. 'I saw the Mile End van bringing the two of you back.'

'I am afraid that Charles has had some bad luck with his car. The engine has packed up and he has to have a new one. So once he has had a drink and some sandwiches, I am driving him back to Penglais. Make yourself comfortable in the sitting room, Charles, and I'll be with you in two ticks.' So saying, I went into the kitchen, where my wife was standing with her hands on her hips.

'Since when have you taken to helping me in the kitchen?' she demanded. 'What's going on?' By the time I had told her about the episode of the Wentworth-Baxter outburst in the study and the subsequent farce of the unoiled engine, Marlene came in with the two children.

'Marlene,' said my wife. 'Could you possibly stay for the next two hours or so? I'll pay you double time if you'll oblige. The Vicar and I have to drive Mr Wentworth-Baxter back to his Vicarage.'

'I don't mind,' replied our baby minder. 'I'm not going out tonight. Come on, kids, let's go up to the nursery.'

After she had gone upstairs with her charges, I turned to Eleanor. 'Now it is my turn to ask what's going on.'

'Well, my dear, from what you have told me, Bronwen is evidently in need of some female support. I know her and it is not like her to go to pieces. Mind, any woman living with Charles for any length of time would have to be a combination of Mother Theresa and Joan of Arc to survive unaffected.'

Half an hour later the three of us were on our way through the countryside, Eleanor and I in front and a glum Charles in the back. He had insisted that he wished to take the back seat. As my wife commented later, it was time that he took that position and stayed there. Evidently, she said, Bronwen and the children had been there long enough.

The evening sun was low in the cloud-streaked sky as we passed the road sign which announced that we were in the village of Penglais. Apart from a few cottages there was nothing else to indicate that we were in a village. Half a mile further on, we turned into the Vicarage drive, a winding weed-afflicted gravelled path, bordered by broken-down fences. As we pulled up outside the porch, a woman with a baby, clad only in a vest, in her arms and surrounded by three unkempt children came to greet us. As she brushed some straggling hair from her forehead, she said unconvincingly, 'What a nice surprise to see you both.' Were it not for the fact that we were at Penglais Vicarage we would have not recognised this slattern as Bronwen.

Then she asked as an afterthought, 'What has happened to our car? Don't tell me that you have had another accident, Charles?'

'Of course not,' he snapped, as if he had never had one. 'Something has gone wrong with the engine, that's all, and I've got to wait to have it repaired in Pontywen.'

As we got out of the car, the three children ran back into the house, as if they were scared of strangers. 'They are very shy, aren't they?' said Eleanor.

'I suppose they are,' replied Bronwen. 'It's because they never see anybody in this God-forsaken hole. I expect you will want to get back to Pontywen now.'

'Do you mind if we come in for a few minutes?' my wife asked. 'It's ages since we have seen you.'

I had never seen anyone so reluctant to say Yes. After a pause, Mrs Wentworth-Baxter, flushed with embarrassment, said, 'Well, only for a few minutes. I've got to get the children to bed and then tidy up all the mess they made everywhere.'

'Mess' was an understatement. The house was indeed a pigsty, as Charles had told me. As soon as we entered the hall, our nostrils were assaulted by a combination of smells, all of them unpleasant. Bronwen, still holding the baby, was about to take us into the sitting room when Eleanor said, 'Perhaps we had better get back. It is getting late. I'll give you a ring tomorrow morning and we'll fix a date for lunch at the Tudor Arms. Charles will mind the children, won't you?' She smiled sweetly at him.

'Of course,' he mumbled.

'I'll come and pick you up sometime next week,' added Eleanor.

'If that's all right with you, Charles,' said Bronwen.

'I've said it's all right, haven't I,' he snarled.

As we drove back to Pontywen my wife was fuming with anger about what she had seen and heard in Penglais Vicarage. 'That man is not only a disaster in a parish. He is an even bigger one in his home. If something is not done soon, the wreckage will be beyond repair.'

'So then, doctor,' I asked, 'what course of treatment do you prescribe?'

'I'll tell you after I have examined the patient next week,' she replied.

5

'I wish we did not have to go?' sighed Eleanor, as she fastened her nylons to her suspender belt. 'I suppose there is no escape since they are both my patients and your parishioners. *C'est la vie.*'

It was the Saturday after our visit to the Wentworth-Baxter Vicarage. Apart from the occasional late wedding, Saturday afternoon and evening provided an opportunity for us to enjoy each other's company without let or hindrance. The majority of weddings were scheduled for the morning or early afternoon and my wife's duties were over by midday. Sometimes she took the children for a drive in the countryside, and once or twice a month Marlene looked after the children to allow the two of us to enjoy a visit to Cardiff or Newport.

Today was different. It was the golden wedding of Mr and Mrs Arthur Davies of Inkerman Street. Edwina Davies was a large talkative lady who was a regular attendant at St Padarn's Church. Her hair was dyed an unnatural black. Thickly applied eyebrow pencil gave her the appearance of a female George Robey. She was liberal in her application of face powder and equally so in her use of rouge. Her thin lips were neatly painted with red lipstick emphasising her rat trap of a mouth, underneath which was a formidable lantern jaw. Long earrings drooped incongruously from her large ears. For a seventy-year-old lady she presented a picture of someone trying to catch up with her youth fifty years late.

Active in the Mothers' Union, the Townswomen's Guild, and the local Labour Party, she was well known in Pontywen as someone to be avoided in the street if discerned on the horizon. Once trapped, there was no escape. 'How are you, Mrs Davies?' would be the signal for her to unfold her medical history, with appropriate quotations from doctors and consultants, going back into the distant past and ending with the very latest diagnosis. In church life, she was the equivalent of Bertie Owen, a Vicar's nightmare, an agitator at meetings and occasionally prone to create a disruption in church. For example, we held our patronal festival earlier that year when the Very Reverend James Williams-Ellis was the preacher. He had been in the pulpit for some twenty minutes, giving a history of the Celtic Church and the place of St Padarn's in its hierarchy. To relieve the boredom Mrs Davies decided to delve into her purse to find a three-penny bit to put on the collection plate. She was not a generous woman. So when she dropped the coin on the floor she began to search for that which she had lost, like the woman in the parable, except that, unlike Edwina, she had mislaid a gold coin. As she bent down to discover the whereabouts of her offering to the Lord, she toppled against the chair of the worshipper in front of her. That lady was jerked forward, so that her head collided with the back of the church warden. This chain reaction halted the preacher as he was about to connect St Padarn with St David.

Despite 'tut-tuts' and 'shushes' from the congregation, she persisted in her attempt to find the coin, her large posterior dislodging her chair, which was pressing into

the knees of Mrs Hughes, the organist's wife, behind her.

'My dear sister,' said the Dean, through gritted teeth, 'would you kindly leave your search for whatever it is you have lost until I have finished my sermon.' By now she was on the floor sweeping it with her hands to try to discover the lost treasure. The remonstrance from the dignitary brought an instant response. Puffing and blowing she struggled to get back into her chair, only to tilt it backwards, landing with her chair in the lap of Mrs Hughes and her legs up in the air. The Dean was still silent, unamused by the circus act of which he had a bird's eye view. In the meanwhile the congregation were beginning to enjoy the diversion, realising that Edwina

Davies was providing more entertainment than St Padarn and St David. All heads were turned towards her and none towards the pulpit. It was with a sense of anticlimax that they resumed their attention to the preacher once order had been restored.

A year previously, the old lady had broken her hip after falling in the street in an attempt to run after the bus which was about to leave the square in Pontywen. This entailed a stay for some months in the local hospital. After causing chaos in the ward, the doctor and the sister were only too pleased to allow her out to attend her granddaughter's wedding in the parish church. Unfortunately the ambulance was late arriving, and everybody, including the bride, was present except Granny Davies. After waiting ten minutes in the porch, I suggested to the bride that it would be advisable to proceed with the service since I had another wedding booked for three quarters of an hour later. 'I wouldn't dare, Vicar,' said the bride. 'You know what my gran is like.' At that moment, the ambulance drew up outside the church gates and soon the old lady was being trundled in her wheelchair up the path.

The customary signal to the organist to begin the Wedding March was the opening of the door at the west end of the church. I had forgotten to warn him about the arrival of Mrs Davies. The door was opened noisily to admit her. 'Here comes the bride,' thundered the organ. The congregation stood and turned to greet her. Instead of a vision in bridal array they saw a flustered old lady in a wheelchair clutching her handbag coming down the aisle and loudly instructing an even more flustered ambulance man to get her down to the front on the bride-side. 'I thought it was supposed to be my day,' said the bride.

These were but two instances of Edwina's ability to draw attention to herself either by accident or design. On the other hand her husband was content to stay out of the limelight, ensconced in his wooden armchair at the fireside and filling the living room with obnoxious fumes from his beloved pipe and its contents of 'Digger's Shag'. He was a little man with a walrus moustache, somewhat discoloured by his tobacco habits. The only time he enjoyed any kudos was in his early married days when he played at outside half for the Pontywen first fifteen. He was good enough to attract the attention of the Cardiff Club. Sadly, Arthur's rugby career came to an abrupt end when his wife paid her first visit to see him play. He was handled with unnecessary vigour by an opposing wing forward and was laid out for a few seconds. On his return home, Edwina threw his boots on the fire and issued an edict that he must never set foot on that field again. He was more afraid of her than any wing forward and a potential international was sacrificed on the altar of matrimonial obedience. As Full Back Jones the grave digger told me, 'If ever there was a martyr, Arthur Davies was one at that time.' Then he added, 'Mind you, he still is.'

The venue for the golden wedding celebration party was the Labour Club, known locally as the 'Glue Pot', from the reluctance of the members to leave there, even after closing time. It was a corrugated-iron structure, which had received its first coat of paint only recently, since its erection in 1933. The Committee had decided on old gold as a suitable shade with scarlet doors and window frames to complete the Labour Party colours. As the Chairman said at the function to mark the occasion,

'We can be proud of our identification with the battle colours of our cause and of the way in which we are brightening up the Valley.' Other inhabitants of Pontywen were not so lyrical about the new look. The Chairman of the British Legion Club described it as 'a bloody red and yellow monstrosity'; Idris the Milk said that it should be known as the 'mustard pot', since so many members got plastered there.

By the time we arrived at the club, there was enough noise coming through the opened windows to be heard in the next valley. Mr and Mrs Davies had four sons, and the three daughters who had begotten twenty-one children, one grandson and two granddaughters had added to the tally by supplying five great-grandchildren. It was obvious that all were present, not to mention well wishers, including the Mayor whose car adorned the car park. As we made our way to the entrance we were almost bowled over by two young boys who were chasing each other and loudly exchanging insults as they ran. It was then that we decided that, as soon as the telegram from the Queen had been read out and the cake had been cut, we would make our excuses and leave the scene as quickly as possible.

Once inside the metal construction, it was difficult to assess which was more unbearable, the temperature or the decibels. To add to the discomfort was the amount of human flesh crammed into such a limited space, which made the Black Hole of Calcutta seem like Wembley Stadium. As we elbowed our way through the throng to discover the whereabouts of the happy couple responsible for the occasion, we were confronted by Bertie Owen who was grinning like a Cheshire Cat. 'She's been waiting for you to come,' he said. 'It will make her evening. By the way, I'm the compère for tonight. Follow me.'

As we followed him, Eleanor murmured, 'That's going to make our evening. Featuring the two biggest bores in Pontywen – Edwina and Bertie.'

'Not only that,' I replied, 'but he makes it sound as if she is a widow. I assume that Arthur must be here, if only in a supporting role.'

After some strenuous physical effort more appropriate to a rugby scrum than the prelude to a meeting with the two people in whose honour the festivities had been arranged, we arrived at a table set out at the foot of the stage. There, in all her glory in a black evening gown of some silky material, with her George Robey facial make up and her fingers decorated with several rings plus purple varnished nails, was Edwina Davies. At her side was an uncomfortable Arthur suffocating in a stiff collar and black bow. On either side of the couple were the Mayor and Mayoress, wearing their chains of office, both sweating profusely and looking as if they were eager to get to their next official engagement.

'The Vicar and Dr Secombe,' announced Bertie.

'I can see that,' said Edwina sharply. 'This is our Vicar and his wife,' she explained to the Mayor and Mayoress.

'We have met before several times when the Vicar was Mayor's Chaplain some years ago,' replied the Mayor.

'I began to think you weren't coming,' she went on. 'We've been holding up proceedings until you were here. There's a nice little do arranged. I think you'll enjoy yourselves. Bertie, bring 'em to order.'

Bertie produced a whistle from his pocket and blew a loud blast. To no avail. The noise continued unabated. It took three more blasts before there was any semblance of order. 'Now then, take your seats, please,' shouted the compère, red in the face after his vigorous blowing. This produced a scramble for the chairs which were lined against the walls. Since the number of persons present was at least three times that of available seats an impromptu game of 'musical chairs' ensued, with the children running around like headless chickens and the adults trying to find their respective family groups, some carrying chairs at the same time. Eventually the chaos subsided. The children sat on the floor and the men either stood behind their seated spouses or joined the large contingent of standing spectators at the back of the hall.

'Now you all know why we are gathered together here today,' began Bertie. 'This is an important occasion. You can tell that by the fact that we have got our chief citizen and his lady wife in our midst. Let's put our hands together and give them a big welcome.' Not enough hands came together to produce a big welcome. It was more in the nature of a polite gesture of goodwill. 'Now then, not only have we got our Mayor and Mayoress here but on this table is a message from our young Queen. I know she hasn't got her crown yet but she is still our sovereign as she is now, whether she is sitting on the throne or not. In a moment or two I will read it out to you. So then, what is all this fuss about? It's because we are honouring two people who have been together for fifty years.' At this point he broke into song: 'And it don't seem a day too much'. After a cough he carried on. 'Mr and Mrs Davies have lived all their lives in Pontywen. Mr Arthur Davies spent all his working life at the Colliery and was in charge of the pit ponies at one time. Mrs

Edwina Davies. Now there's a lady for you. Everybody in Pontywen knows Edwina. The Labour Party, the Mothers' Union, the Townswomen's Guild, St Padarn's Parochial Church Council. You name it, she's in it and at her age too.' Edwina frowned. 'I'm hoping she'll do her party piece for us later on to show how young in heart she is.' Edwina smiled a thin-lipped smile.

'Heaven preserve us,' whispered my wife.

'I could go on for the rest of the evening telling of all the things she has done for the people of Pontywen but we have a long programme arranged to celebrate this golden wedding.'

By now his audience was getting restive. 'Well, get on with it, Bertie,' shouted someone at the back of the hall.

'So then, without any more ado, I will read out the message from Her Majesty the Queen.' Bertie took the large envelope from the table and extracted the telegram. He made a great show of taking his spectacles from his pocket and placing them on his red nose. He cleared his throat and took a deep breath. "Heartiest congratulations on your golden wedding. Elizabeth R".'

'Is that it?' said Idris the Milk, who was standing near by.

'I now call on his Worship the Mayor to say a few words before he leaves for another engagement further down the valley.'

Alderman William Evans rose to his feet with alacrity, ready to make a quick getaway. 'Mr and Mrs Davies, you have reached a great millstone – er – milestone in your lives. Not many marriages go on as long as yours has done. Yet here you are surrounded by your family and your friends having survived fifty years of being together in the – er – estate of matrimony. I hope you have a happy evening and that you will have many more years of – er – being together. Good night to you all.'

He turned to the Mayoress, who was bestowing a kiss on Edwina's countenance. 'Come on, Annie,' he said to her, 'we're late already. We don't want to keep them waiting at the Chamber of Trade dinner, like we did last week at the Co-op dinner dance.'

'Give them one more clap,' requested Bertie. That is precisely what they had, contributed by me as a solo effort.

Once they had left, the noise reached deafening proportions again, prompting the use of the compère's whistle. When the pandemonium had been reduced to a tolerable level of murmured conversation, Bertie was on his feet. 'Next,' he shouted, 'I will ask the Vicar to say a few words.'

'Another of your occupational hazards,' said Eleanor out of the side of her mouth.

'Mr and Mrs Davies, relatives and friends. I am not going to keep you long,' I began.

'Hear! Hear!' came from several quarters.

'You were married not long after the turn of this century. During that time the world has become a different place. It has shrunk into a globe which aeroplanes can encircle in a matter of days and the wireless in a couple of seconds. For you your world has been one tiny dot on that little globe. Pontywen is that dot but it has been big enough to provide you with a large family and all the love that comes with it. Congratulations to you both and may that love continue to be with you until the end of your days, whatever changes that time will bring. God bless you and keep you.'

No sooner had I finished my 'few words' than there was a concerted dash towards the bar at the side of the hall. Bertie indicated to Eleanor and myself that we should occupy the seats vacated by the Mayor and Mayoress. We looked at each other and acknowledged that we were trapped. We would be unable to emulate the chief citizen and his wife and escape whatever else the evening had to unfold. 'Thank you, Vicar,' said Edwina as I sat beside her. 'That was very nice. Now they will bring the refreshments out on to the tables. We didn't have them brought out before, otherwise the kids would have been eating everything in sight before you could look round. You know what they're like. We'll have the cake cut later on. Perhaps you'll say grace when everything is ready.' Two long tables were set out on either side of the hall, covered with a mixture of lace and plain tablecloths brought from the various homes of the Davies progeny. Soon the daughters and daughters-in-law emerged from the kitchen carrying trays loaded with sandwiches, cakes and trifles.

Whilst I sat and listened to Mrs Davies's non-stop monologue Eleanor was making a vain attempt to engage Arthur in conversation. His contribution to the *tête-à-tête* consisted of monosyllables delivered from a face more appropriate to a funeral than a golden wedding celebration. It was obvious that Edwina had forbidden him to bring his beloved foul-smelling pipe. Add to that deprivation the discomfort of the stiff collar and it was small wonder that he was longing for the return to his armchair. His countenance grew longer by the minute. The din caused by the shouting and the antics of the excited children, plus the loud laughter and badinage coming from the alcoholic contingent around the bar, was reaching an unbearable level. It was a great relief when Alice the eldest daughter came up to us and announced that the food was ready.

'Quiet!' bellowed her mother. She had a strong contralto voice which rivalled that of Dame Clara Butt. It caused more of a hush than the compère's whistle. 'Come and get your plates filled.' A stampede ensued, led by the hungry children. Our table was already laden with the festive fare.

'Help yourselves,' commanded Edwina. 'When you've done that I'll ask Bertie to get you to say grace, Vicar.'

'I don't think you'll need him, Mrs Davies,' I replied. 'You are much more in charge than he is.'

'You've got to have a compère at the club,' she said. 'He offered his services and I didn't want to offend him.' I was about to add that Bertie always offered his services because no one else would ever recommend him but thought better of it when my wife gave me one of her reproving looks.

It must have taken at least a quarter of an hour before Mrs Davies decided to call upon the services of the compère.

'Now I will call upon the Vicar to say grace. Will you all stand, please,' he announced in lay-reader tones. Since most people were standing already and those who were sitting were trying to balance plates on their laps and hold a drink at the same time, it caused some confusion and a few upturned plates of sandwiches.

I attempted to say an impromptu prayer suitable for

the occasion. 'For these thy gifts of food, O Lord, and for all the blessings of this life, especially for those which thou hast bestowed upon these two persons, gathered together here.' I stopped and coughed as I realised that it was impossible for two persons to gather together. '. . . present here, in the midst of their loved ones.' I decided to call it a day. 'Amen,' I said and sat down. I could see that my wife was struggling to stifle an outburst of laughter.

'Thank you, Vicar,' said Edwina. 'That was lovely, wasn't it, Arthur?' He nodded and ate a sandwich. I suppose that as long as he filled his mouth with food, he thought there would be no need for him to speak.

The next item in what Bertie called 'a long programme' was the cutting of the cake. Alice brought to the top table a large iced cake with fifty candles on it. 'She made that herself,' said Edwina, 'and our Liz did the icing. Our Mary bought the candles. They're good girls, aren't they?'

'I must say, they have made a great job of it,' Eleanor replied.

'Liz was up all last night, doing the icing with all those fiddly bits, wasn't she, Alice?'

'Not as long as I was making the cake,' she said petulantly to her mother.

'There you are all three of you getting together to make a wonderful tribute to your mother and father,' I commented, in an effort to keep the peace.

'Let's hope it tastes as good as it looks.' The matriarch's remark evoked a scowl from her eldest.

'Suck it and see,' was her response as she walked away.

'We are now going to light the cake,' Bertie told his

audience. 'We' were Liz and Mary, who advanced upon the work of art with a box of matches each.

'You take that side, Mary,' ordered Liz. After contending with a number of stubborn wicks, eventually all the candles were lit by the sisters, who stood admiring their handiwork.

'Mr and Mrs Davies will now blow out the fifty candles,' shouted Bertie. Edwina's quota was soon extinguished.

'Shall I help,' said Eleanor to Arthur. He nodded with his mouth still half full. She completed his task with myself grateful for deliverance from whatever might be blown in my direction. Everybody clapped and cheered.

'Come on, Mam and Dad, cut the cake, then,' said Liz. 'You've got the knife by there.'

'All right, calm down,' replied her mother. 'I can see where the knife is. Stand up, Arthur, you've got to help me.' Her husband rose reluctantly. 'Put your hand over mine and I'll do the rest.' She pressed the knife firmly into the cake. Once again there were cheers and claps.

'It's a pity the photographer from the *Gazette* isn't here,' Eleanor said.

'He came to the house this morning to take a picture of us with the telegram from the Queen,' Edwina replied. 'I suppose he couldn't come twice. In any case, I expect he's down at that hotel with the Mayor and Mayoress. The Chamber of Trade is more important than a couple of pensioners having a "do" in the Labour Club. The nobs always come first.'

'Raise your glasses and drink to Edwina and Arthur,' said Bertie. Eleanor and I looked at each other as we drank a modicum of sweet British sherry from the thimble glasses provided, grateful that it was confined to a modicum.

When we sat down Edwina said to me, 'Thank you for the grace and your little speech.' She sipped at her sherry. 'It's very nice, isn't it?'

I felt ashamed at the smug way I had looked at my wife, scorning the drink which celebrated the occasion. I remembered my parents, my aunts and my uncles when I was a boy, to whom a Christmas cheap sherry was one of the highlights of the festive season. 'Very nice indeed,' I replied.

'Drink that, Arthur,' said one of his former workmates as he put a pint of beer in front of him. 'You deserve that after fifty years of penal servitude. Sorry, Edwina, only joking.' He departed rapidly, leaving Arthur with a foaming tankard in front of him and a glowering wife beside him. Such was her husband's desperation that he chose to seize the receptacle and empty its contents with barely a pause in the process. For a little man with a restrictive collar it was a most impressive performance.

His wife looked at him as if she were seeing a different person from the one with whom she had shared fifty years of married life. 'You'll be up all night after that, Arthur Davies,' she warned him.

'Do you know what, Edwina?' he replied. 'I think I'll have another one. I enjoyed that.'

'Would you let me buy you another one?' asked Eleanor.

'Thank you, doctor,' he said quickly before his spouse could intervene.

As my wife went to the bar, Edwina said to me, 'Well, Vicar, I hope my husband realises what he is doing. He only rarely drinks except at Christmas and then only a drop of sherry like just now. Perhaps the doctor thinks he is used to drinking.'

'I don't think one more pint will do him any harm, will it, Mr Davies?' I replied.

'I used to drink a lot more than that when I played rugby.' It was the first full sentence Arthur had spoken that evening.

'And a lot of good that did you,' snapped his wife. 'You leave it at one more, "boyo".'

My wife returned with a tray full of drinks. A pint for 'boyo', a sherry for Edwina, and two whiskies for ourselves. 'I hope a sherry is what you want, Mrs Davies,' she said.

'Lovely,' was the reply. 'Thank you, doctor. It's very kind of you. I've been telling Arthur that he mustn't have any more after this. It will go to his head otherwise. You see, he doesn't drink normally.'

'I could see that,' said my wife. 'Still, one more pint won't hurt him.'

At this point in the conversation, Bertie arrived to tell us that he was about to introduce the entertainment. 'Do you want to do your party piece first or later in the programme,' he asked Edwina. 'The pianist has got the music for you.'

'I think I had better do it now before I get too tired,' she said, and made her way from the table to the side of the little stage.

Eleanor came and sat by me. 'What is the betting it is a Clara Butt rendering of "Home Sweet Home"?' she whispered.

In the meanwhile Arthur had swallowed his second

pint. 'We had better move our chairs, Mr Davies, to have a better view,' I suggested.

'You can,' he replied, 'but I see it every Christmas.'

'It doesn't sound like "Home Sweet Home" to me,' I said to my wife.

A few minutes later the compère appeared in front of the curtains. 'Put your hands together and give a big welcome to the Belle of the Ball for this evening, Edwina Davies!' The curtains opened to reveal the lady standing centre stage and acknowledging the applause with a bow.

'Ready!' shouted the pianist.

'Off you go,' she shouted back. He launched into a version of the sailors' hornpipe. Soon the performer was in full swing from climbing the ropes to pulling them but, when she decided to fold her arms and dance with her legs outstretched, with her bottom almost at floor level, Eleanor expressed some alarm.

'Her hip,' she murmured. The alarm was justified. Suddenly Edwina was stretched out on the floor, in agony. The curtain came across and my wife was up on the stage seconds later. There was an apprehensive silence.

'It's her own fault,' said Arthur about his partner of fifty years. 'She's too headstrong, that's her trouble. I told her not to do it but she wouldn't listen.'

When I arrived on the scene, all the Davies family were there, surrounding their mother. 'She has dislocated her hip once again,' said my wife to me. Then she addressed the throng. 'I think it's best that you all go back to your places in the hall. The steward has rung for the ambulance and it should be here before long.'

'Where's Arthur?' demanded the patient. Liz pushed her way through the curtains.

'Dad,' she shouted to her father who was finishing his third pint, with his collar undone and his bow tie dangling down his shirt front, 'Mam wants to see you.'

'I'm coming,' he replied and made his way slowly up the steps to the stage.

'What do you look like, Arthur Davies?' said his wife, her face contorted with pain but with her tongue still razor sharp. 'Liz, do his collar up and put his tie right. I told you not to drink any more. You'd better come with me to the hospital. Then you won't be able to wet your whistle. When you've seen to his collar, Liz, tell Bertie Owen to carry on with the programme once the ambulance has taken me.'

It was not long before the ambulance arrived. They took her out through the side entrance to avoid parading her through the hall. As some Valley news reporter remarked of a funeral, 'The death had cast a gloom over the proceedings.' Despite the best efforts of Bertie to carry on with the programme it was like a performance of *Hamlet* without the Prince.

Eleanor and I made our apologies to the family and left early. As we drove home, I said to her, 'What a dotty thing to do with her hip in that condition!'

'You should have expected that after what you said in your "few words",' she replied.

'What do you mean?' I asked.

'Well, you said that Pontywen was a dot on the globe. In which case everybody who lives in it must be dotty.'

'Very funny, Eleanor.'

'You don't sound amused, Frederick. Never mind, love, at least we have avoided Bertie telling us to put our hands together several more times during the rest of the evening. I am sure he thought he was back in charge of St Padarn's Sunday School.'

'And he made as much of a mess of that as he did of the celebrations tonight.'

'Vicar, you are in a mood. You had better get rid of that by tomorrow. Otherwise your congregation will not know what has hit them.'

'Only playing,' I said.

'You weren't, you know,' she replied, 'but I love you just the same.'

6

'It's not going to be a nice morning. I've given you fair warning,' announced Jack the Fish as he arrived on our doorstep. Jack Williams, travelling fishmonger, came once a week to the Vicarage in his ancient van, bringing fresh fish collected early that morning from the trawlers' catches at Swansea Docks. It was always a nostalgic occasion for me. I had spent my boyhood amongst the trawler men and the dockers when we lived in our council house overlooking Swansea Bay. Unfortunately the nostalgia was tempered by the inane rhyming inflicted on his customers by the little man, adorned in his striped apron and sporting his battered straw boater.

'Now what shall it be today? I can offer you some cod or some ray or perhaps a steak of hake.' His beady little eyes looked past me as Eleanor came behind me. 'Ah. The lady of the house, come to assist her reverend spouse.'

'Now then, Jack,' said my wife, 'if you keep on like this you can take your fresh fish back.'

'Very good, Dr Secombe.' His expression made it plain that he thought Eleanor was not in the same league of poets as himself.

'Since my husband will be dining alone for lunch, I should think a small steak of hake will not my pocket break.' This second attempt at verse had a much more appreciative acceptance. 'By the way,' she added, 'I hope your weather forecast is incorrect. I have to drive into the countryside to pick up someone who needs sunshine, not rain.' As she paid him for the fish, he ended the transaction with a typical flourish.

'I know my forecast of coming rain has caused you mental pain. I can only hope my wireless set from which my weather news I get is wrong about the rain, as it is again and again.'

As he drove off up the drive, I said to Eleanor, 'I think he should have his meter examined.'

'I would have said it is his head, Fred.' She burst into laughter. 'See how contagious his rhyming is, if you'll pardon my effort.'

'I'm afraid that is unpardonable by any priest, including your husband,' I replied.

Half an hour later, she was on her way to pick up Bronwen Wentworth-Baxter for their lunch date, leaving me with the task of coping with our two children since it was Marlene's day off. Mrs Watkins was preparing my 'steak of hake' and its garnishments. Elspeth, our baby daughter, had been fed and watered by her mother and was soundly asleep in her cot. David, our three-year-old son, had come with me to the front door to wave goodbye to his mother. He was a sturdy child who had grown out of his habit of trying to eat lumps of coal and of using his head as a hammer against the wall of his bedroom. Eleanor explained that the latter was due to the protracted labour which brought him into the world, caused by the largeness of his head, inherited from his father. I had strict instructions to put him to bed at three o'clock, despite any protestations he might make. I was looking forward to the next few hours in his company. He had ceased to be a baby and had become a little boy who could carry on a conversation.

'What about a game of football, David?' I suggested.

'Yes, please,' he said enthusiastically. 'Can I be the goalie, Dad? I like being the goalie. Don't kick the ball too hard, though.'

'I promise I won't,' I replied. He ran back into the house to get the ball from the play room upstairs. As he did so, the telephone rang. 'Pontywen 342,' I said. I suppose I should have said 'Vicar of Pontywen speaking' or 'Pontywen Vicarage'. For some psychological reason, I preferred to remain anonymous, unlike the porter at St Woolos Hospital in Newport who always picked up the phone and announced that he was 'St Woolos'.

'Is that by chance the Vicar of Pontywen?' inquired a lady whose accent was distinctly transatlantic. The shock of encountering a voice from the New World stunned me into a momentary silence. 'Hello! Are you there?' she continued.

'Yes, indeed. This is the Vicar of Pontywen,' I replied in the best ecclesiastical manner I could manage.

'Vicar, I am Mrs Susannah Price from Austin, Texas and I am over here for a few months taking in Europe and coming back for your wonderful coronation on 2 June.' Before I could explain that it was not mine she launched into a long account of her reason for contacting the Vicar of Pontywen. Apparently her great-grandfather had been a miner at Pontywen Colliery and his son had emigrated to the United States in 1882 to find work in the coal mines of Pennsylvania. She was married to a lawyer who was also of Welsh extraction and they were both 'enjoying a pilgrimage back to their roots,' as she put it.

At this juncture in the conversation, David came into earshot shouting, 'Dad! Come on! I've got the ball.'

I put my hand over the receiver. 'You go out on the lawn and I'll be with you in two ticks,' I told him. 'Excuse me,' I said to her, 'that was my young son wanting me to play football with him.'

'How cute,' she gushed.

'Well, Mrs Price, what can I do for you?' I asked.

'My husband and I are coming to Cardiff next week. He is going to the Rhondda to try to trace his roots and I am coming to Pontywen to trace mine.' It sounded more like a botanical expedition than a pilgrimage. 'I don't want to hold up your little boy's game. Shall I just say that I shall be in Pontywen next Monday and I should like to have a look at your church registers and the tombstones in your church cemetery some time in the afternoon, if it is convenient.'

'By all means,' I replied. 'Shall we say three thirty?'

'OK by me,' she said, 'and thank you for all your help. See you Monday, Vicar.'

I put the phone down and turned to face David who was looking at me with his large white football clasped against his stomach. 'Come on then, Dad,' he demanded. 'Mrs Watkins says we mustn't be too long because dinner will be ready soon.'

'In that case,' I said, 'we had better get cracking, otherwise she'll be giving us a row and we don't want that, do we?' He shook his head.

We moved out on the balcony with David hugging the football to his chest. 'Come on then,' I shouted, 'throw me the ball.'

'I'm not ready yet,' said my son. 'I've got to go and get my gloves.'

On the few occasions I had taken him to see Pontywen United play in the local league, Dai Phillips, the goal-keeper, the younger son of Phillips the Grocer, always wore gloves and made a great show of adjusting them every five minutes or so. While I waited for him to come back with his gloves, there was a click as the Vicarage gates were opened and Emlyn Howells, my curate, came down the drive. His normal high colour had intensified into a deep puce.

As he walked across the lawn to me, I could see that his breathing was causing him distress. 'Vicar,' he gasped. 'Sorry to trouble you, but I have just been in the vestry to write in the details for tomorrow's wedding and the safe has gone. What's more, the carpet down the aisle has disappeared with it.'

There had been only one 'break in' since I came to the parish eight years ago and that was at the tin church of St Padarn's, perpetrated by two young boys from the local council estate – a piece of juvenile bravado. Evidently this was much more sinister and much more brazen. The church adjoined the Vicarage and I had been in the church for morning service at eight o'clock, accompanied by my curate. Four hours later, despite my living next door to the church, thieves had managed to carry away a very heavy safe and a long length of carpet in full daylight without anyone being aware of what had happened. By now David had appeared, wearing his winter gloves, and still carrying his beloved football. 'Ready, Dad?' he asked.

Emlyn and I rushed into the Vicarage, leaving my son bewildered on the lawn. I dialled '999' and waited impatiently for the answer. 'Your local constable will be there shortly. The CID will be along later on.'

'Would you mind playing football with David while I go and see for myself what has happened?' I asked the curate. 'By the way, you have to dribble with the ball and then shoot, gently, of course, at the goalkeeper.'

'He won't have any trouble saving the ball. I'm the world's worst footballer,' he replied. 'Not only that, I'm out of breath.'

When I entered the church it was quite a shock to see the bare stone floor of the aisle. The expensive red carpet had been a gift to celebrate the centenary of the church. Inside the safe were the solid silver chalice, paten and flagon presented to the church at its opening one hundred and four years ago. So, too, were the church registers covering that period. Since I always kept the church open for private prayer during the daylight hours, and the vestry door had no lock, it would be a simple exercise to remove the safe. The patch of wall against which it had reposed displayed a lack of paint and a plethora of ancient webs long vacated by the spiders.

As I waited for Will Book and Pencil, PC William Davies, the local constable, I remembered the phone call of earlier that morning and the lady from Austin, Texas, who was due to inspect the registers on Monday afternoon. My musings were interrupted by heavy footsteps down the stone floor accompanied by much puffing and blowing, heralding the arrival of the strong arm of law. Six foot tall and solidly built, he was a formidable figure but whose physical stature was not commensurate with his mental capacity.

'You haven't touched anything, have you, Vicar?' he said, as he came through the door of the vestry.

'There is nothing for me to touch,' I replied. 'The

vestry door was open and so was the door at the west end. What amazes me is how they were able to carry that very heavy safe out of the church.'

He pondered that problem for a while. 'Perhaps the safe wasn't all that heavy and if you had two strong men they would be able to carry it. Mind, they wouldn't be able to carry it down the street without being detected. So they must have had some kind of van to take it away.' He produced his famous note book from his pocket and then his pencil from inside his jacket. 'Do you mind if I sit down, Vicar?' he inquired and then moved a chair beside the desk.

'Excuse me saying this, PC Davies,' I said to him, 'but shouldn't you have avoided touching that chair in case there were fingerprints on it?'

'Oh, I doubt if they would touch the chair; they wouldn't need to do that. I'm more concerned about fingerprints on the door handles. Now then, do you keep the church locked?'

'No, Constable. I have always believed that the church should be open to anyone who wishes to come in and say their private prayers. A number of people have told me how grateful they were to come into the quiet and sanctity in times of personal distress. Others just want to sit down and get away from it all, without saying any prayer. My predecessors kept the church open for that purpose and I intend to follow their example.'

He pursed his lips and then looked me in the eye. 'In that case, Vicar, you can't say anything if the place gets burgled. It's an invitation to any crook who happens to be around. Well, I tell you what, if you are going to leave the church open, the least you can do is to see that the vestry is locked up. I know it is like locking the stable door after the horse has bolted, but there you are. Now then, Vicar, what were the contents of the safe.' Laboriously he took down all the details about the safe and the carpet. Then he said, 'The boys from the CID will be here before long. In the meantime, I'll go and make inquiries around the houses in Church Street to see if they noticed anything suspicious. I shouldn't be surprised if somebody or other has seen something.'

I sat down in my seat in the chancel and stared at the table on the wall opposite. 'To the glory of God and in memory of Joseph Lloyd Morgan, Vicar of Pontywen 1871 to 1898. A faithful pastor and a friend of the fatherless and widows.' How many fatherless and widows were the price paid to King Coal, I wondered. What is more, how would Joseph Lloyd Morgan react if he were in my shoes? Would he consider that the loss of a safe and a carpet were a price worth paying to provide a place of prayer for those who needed it? I could almost hear him saying, 'Don't let a couple of thieves shut down your church, my boy. The Holy Communion does not depend upon the quality of silver. It is simply the giving of consecrated bread and wine, just as valid if it comes from an ordinary plate and a cup as it would be from the most valuable of antique silver.'

Before I could congratulate myself further on my policy of an open church, the two plain clothes men of the CID entered the church. I came out of my stall and went to meet them as they came down the aisle, instantly recognisable by their height and their feet. They were younger than 'Will Book and Pencil' and seemed to be more intelligent.

'I am Detective Sergeant Wilcox,' said the red-faced corpulent one of the duo, 'and this is my colleague, Detective Constable Pugh.' The junior member of the partnership was taller but considerably thinner. As a choreographer at a weekend drama school I attended in the Valley once informed us, people can be divided into balls and pins. Sergeant Wilcox was decidedly a large ball while Detective Pugh would have made an excellent Cleopatra's Needle.

'So, you've had a little bit of trouble, Vicar.' The detective sergeant made it sound as if someone had walked off with a hymn book.

'More than a little bit, I would say,' I replied. 'That safe contained valuable silver Communion vessels and all the registers dating back more than a hundred years. The carpet can be replaced but not the contents of the safe.'

'Obviously a professional job. We'll get our fingerprint man out here but I should think they would have used gloves in any case. It was the silver they were after and just took your nice carpet as a bonus. I take it that you leave the church open.'

'Yes, I feel it should always be there as a place of comfort for anybody who needs it.'

'And a place of profit for any thief,' said Detective Pugh.

His colleague ignored that remark and proceeded with his interrogation. 'When were you last in the church?'

'My curate and I were here at eight o'clock this morning for our daily service.'

'When was the theft discovered?'

'The curate went to the church about twelve o'clock to fill in details for a wedding tomorrow. He came to tell me and I dialled 999 immediately. What amazes me,' I said, 'was how they could remove such a heavy safe.'

'Easy,' he replied. 'They probably used a trolley. With a van outside and a ramp to wheel the trolley, the whole operation would be over in a matter of minutes. Now then, has there been any publicity at all about your valuable church silver?'

'Not that I know of, Sergeant. I think there was a mention of it when we celebrated our centenary four years ago but nothing since then. I do mention it in the little guide I have written for visitors to the church, not that we have many in Pontywen.'

'May I see it, Vicar?' he asked.

I took him down to the shelves at the back of the church where we kept copies of the parish magazine on the ledge over the rows of hymn books and prayer books. He thumbed through the few pages of the guide. In it I had written, 'The only treasures in this parish church are the elaborate chalice paten and flagon in sterling silver presented by Sir David Jones-Williams, in 1849.'

'Well, Vicar,' said the detective, 'unless they are securely protected, it is an open invitation to any thief to take them. In the years to come, if churches are going to look after their treasures they will have to take adequate safeguards to protect them. In other words, if you don't mind me saying so, you are asking for trouble. There's a big wide world outside and the people in it are not like those inside a church. As you can see from what has happened here.'

As we spoke, Will Book and Pencil made a noisy entrance, looking very pleased with himself and producing his beloved note book from his pocket excitedly in his

progress down the aisle. 'I've just come from number 4, Church Street, where somebody witnessed the robbery, without realising that it was one,' he announced when he came up to us. 'Mrs Myfanwy Hopkins said that when she was making the bed in the front room, she happened to look out of the window. She saw two men in white coats pulling a trolley down the church path, with a large object on it, covered by what looked like some kind of carpet. They opened the back of a white van which was outside. One of them bent into it and pulled out some kind of metal support. They then pushed the trolley up it, closed the door and went off. I asked her what they looked like. She said that one was about thirty, short and fair haired and the other was older, about forty, with a dark moustache and dark hair. He was bigger than the other one. She thought it was somebody doing repair work in the church. I asked her what time it was when she saw them. She said she thought it must have been about ten thirty since that was the time she always made the beds. Nobody else in the street had noticed anything.' He put his notebook in his pocket with an air of achievement.

'Thank you, Will. That confirms what I thought had happened,' said the senior detective. 'I am afraid, Vicar, that you will not see your valuable silver again. By tomorrow, it will probably have been melted down somewhere. On the other hand, I shouldn't be surprised if your registers turn up somewhere in the vicinity of Pontywen in the next day or so. Let's hope they will not be exposed to the elements for too long. I am afraid there is not much more we can do at the moment. We shall let you know immediately if we find anything.' He shook hands with me and went off briskly accompanied by his lanky colleague who managed to catch him up by the church door.

'I'd better be getting off, too,' said Will Book and Pencil. 'Sorry about this, Vicar, but that's how it goes. I'll have a look round down the dell later on. It's surprising what you can find down there sometimes.' The 'dell' was a little wooded ravine on the outskirts of the town, frequented by courting couples and those who wished to dispose of unwanted items of household equipment.

When I left the church, I did something I had never done before. I locked it. The thought of the house of God being open to desecration suddenly made me feel guilty of dereliction. 'What I shall do,' I said to myself, 'is to put up a notice outside the church informing anyone who wishes to use the building for private prayer or meditation they could obtain the key from the Vicarage.' If I was not at home, there was always Eleanor or Mrs Watkins available.

To my surprise, I found Emlyn Howells and David still engaged in a game of football on the lawn. 'This is a long game,' I said.

'To be honest,' replied the curate, 'we have only just restarted after half time when Mrs Watkins brought us some pop and a biscuit.'

'I've saved all the goals, Dad,' said my son proudly.

'They need him in the Welsh team against England next week,' gasped Emlyn, as he ran to secure the ball David had thrown into the rose bushes.

'Dinner's ready,' shouted Mrs Watkins, as she saw us on the lawn.

'I don't want any, Dad,' said David.

'I should think not, too,' chided our domestic help. 'You've already had your pop and biscuits. This is for your father.'

'What do the police say,' asked Emlyn, clutching the football.

'Apparently the theft is the work of professionals and it is extremely doubtful if we shall recover the Communion set. However, the detectives said that it is most likely that we shall be able to get the registers back, discarded somewhere after the safe had been broken open. Will Book and Pencil is going to search the dell to see what he can find.'

'Let's hope he can do that by tomorrow. How on earth

can the marriage take place tomorrow if there is no marriage register?' the curate enquired. 'There has to be some kind of official form to be signed.'

'I think the first thing I have to do is to phone David Fitzgerald to get his advice. There must be some kind of procedure in a case like this. When I have done that I had better have my dinner before Mrs Watkins gets at me.' The diocesan register was very helpful. He told me to use the return forms which came every quarter from the local register office. Then, if the registers were recovered, the bride and groom and the two witnesses would have to come back and sign them. Otherwise, the signatures would have to be made in the new registers.

Our domestic help was looking disgruntled when I went into the kitchen for my meal. 'Your dinner's not very warm. I would have put it in the oven if I had known you was going to go on that old phone again.' No sooner had I tasted my first mouthful of hake than there was a ring on the doorbell. Mrs Watkins exploded, 'You carry on, Vicar. I'll go to the door. I'll tell them you are having your dinner.' She stamped out of the room with David at her heels. She was back in an instant. 'It's Will Book and Pencil with those books that have been stolen. I'd better put your dinner in the oven.'

'You had, indeed,' I shouted joyfully as I jumped to my feet. 'Come on in PC, Davies. What an angel of mercy you are!' I effused. The constables's cup of self-satisfaction was overflowing at his second triumph of detection that morning. He put down the registers on my desk.

'There you are, Vicar, intact as far as I can see. It's a good job it's dry today. They were out in the open, alongside your safe down in the dell. They had bashed in the back of the safe and the Communion cup and plate and flagon have gone of course. Anyway you've got your registers back. Well, if you don't mind I'll be on my way. If you don't mind me saying so once again, you'll have to start locking the church up if you want to look after the contents. Next time it could be the candlesticks and the cross.' He strode up the drive with the jauntiness of a man of achievement, a Sherlock Holmes with yet another case solved.

When Eleanor returned from her lunch with Bronwen a few hours later, she was looking unusually serious.

'You have missed all the excitement, love,' I said as she came through the door.

'I could do with some exciting news after all the tale of woe I have been hearing. Tell me your story and then I'll tell you mine,' she replied and then listened to my account of the brazen theft and of Will Book and Pencil's starring role in the thriller. 'So the church is minus its valuable silver and its expensive carpet but our local constable has retrieved the left-overs,' she commented.

'Oh! be fair,' I replied. 'They are not just left-overs. All the history of Pontywen church is contained in these registers – all the baptisms, the marriages and the details of every service that has taken place within its hallowed walls.'

'My! we are waxing poetic, aren't we? Well, I wish that I could be as poetic about all the stories I have heard about your erstwhile colleague,' she said in acid tones. It was not like Eleanor to be so bitter.

'I think you had better tell me what you have heard from Bronwen. Evidently it is not exactly the happiest of sagas.' We were sitting together on the settee in the lounge. I put my hand on top of hers and clutched it tightly. For a while she said nothing and then, after a deep breath, she began.

'Charles Wentworth-Baxter is a lazy, self-indulgent brute and I mean brute, Fred, a brute. That poor girl has had to put up with verbal and occasionally physical abuse. Apparently he has forced his attentions upon her as soon as he could after each child has been born. He has not hit her but he has gripped her by the arms in some of his rages. The bruises are still evident. He has forbidden her to get in touch with her mother because he says that she will only cause trouble since she is a strict Baptist and did not want her to marry him in the first place. He has hit little Llewellyn across the face, leaving marks there for hours afterwards. He is very rarely in the house and when he does come home he expects a meal to be ready for him instantly. That girl is going through hell, Fred.'

She began to cry. I put my arms around her and cuddled her. 'As a doctor,' she said, 'I should be able to look at their domestic scene dispassionately but I can't. We know them too intimately. What can we do, Fred? If something is not done soon, she will either put a carving knife into him or, if she is wise, she will take the children with her and take refuge with her mother. Either way it is the end of their marriage.'

We sat in silence for a while. 'There are two alternatives,' I replied. 'The first is that I confront the lion in his den. I have done that already – not in his den, admittedly. I am sure that will be counter-productive. The other is that I should get in touch with the Bishop and let him know what is happening in Penglais Vicarage. I think that is the only way to approach this. The Bishop knows Charles and all his deficiencies. I hope that he will deliver him an ultimatum. If Charles does not comply then he will have to leave Penglais and his family. I am sure her mother will take her back but with an attitude of 'I told you so'. At least she will have some comfort from her father who loves her and has the distinct advantage of being a sensible person and a non-strict Baptist.'

We decided that this was the best course to follow and that I should ring the Bishop the next morning. When I went to church for service the following day I was able to assure Emlyn Howells that he could proceed with the wedding that afternoon without any difficulty. 'I must say,' he told me, 'I take my hat off to Will Book and Pencil for that piece of detection. It is not often he gets an accolade for anything.'

'Oh, he is quite proud of it,' I replied. 'He left the Vicarage yesterday afternoon with all the aplomb of a Sexton Blake or Sherlock Holmes. By the way, I think it wiser to keep the church locked as from now on. I shall get you a key made. Now we have to buy a new safe, a new Communion set and a new carpet for the aisle. I wonder if our transatlantic visitor will be able to help in this direction.'

'Who is that?' he enquired. When I told him, he said, 'If this is any encouragement, Vicar, a lady from Chicago whose ancestors were buried in the churchyard of my last parish paid for the renovation of the organ and the rebuilding of the churchyard wall.'

'Emlyn, you are a tower of strength to your Vicar,' I replied. 'I only wish you could have come as a curate before Charles Wentworth-Baxter was foisted upon the parish. It would have saved me, the parish and his wife and children a great deal of aggravation.

When I went back to the Vicarage, Eleanor was on the phone, looking very agitated. 'I'll be with you in half an hour,' she said, and rang off. 'That was Bronwen. There was quite a scene after I dropped her off at the Vicarage. Charles accused her of letting us try to run her life. Then this morning things erupted once again. Only this time he turned violent and gave her a black eye. He stormed out, got into the car and drove off. She is getting the children ready to take them to her mother. Since she hasn't any transport, she has asked me to pick them up. What a mess! Her mother hasn't a phone so she has rung her aunt who lives a few doors away. Mrs Williams is going to have quite a shock because Bronwen has told her nothing of what has been happening.'

A few minutes later, she was in her car. She wound down the window. 'Sorry to leave you with the children once again. Marlene should be along soon anyway. Keep your fingers crossed that our friend Charles has not returned by the time I get there.' Then she was up the drive, ploughing up the gravel as she shot off from the starting mark, leaving my call to the Bishop in abeyance. As Will Book and Pencil had said about the need for ensuring that the theft in the church would not be repeated, it would be like locking up the stable door after the horse had bolted.

7

She was a short, corpulent, ageing, peroxide blond with an expensive coiffure, and even more expensive outfit which was fighting a losing battle with her figure. The taxi driver who had driven her from Cardiff General station asked me if I could recommend a good café for 'something to eat' while he waited to transport his fare back to the capital city. His face gave the happy expression of a man who had struck oil, as he left his cab to walk to Cascarini's in Pontywen Square.

Mrs Susannah Price of Austin, Texas arrived at the Vicarage punctually at the appointed time of 3.30 p.m. As the taxi driver walked up the drive she stood on the doorstep, admiring the lawn and the rose bushes, which had come into flower only recently. 'You certainly live in a green and pleasant land, as your poet says,' she commented.

Eleanor said afterwards, 'Perhaps she thinks that Wales is just a province of England, in which case we could claim Blake as one of our bards.'

'Where is your little boy?' asked our visitor when she came into the lounge. 'He sounded so cute asking you to play football when you were on the phone.'

'He's in bed,' replied my wife. 'David is only three and needs his afternoon sleep.'

'Have you any other children?'

'One daughter, Elspeth. She is only six months old and

is also aloft. This is what we call our breathing space, an hour or so's peace before it is disrupted once again. Still, they are both good children, if you count a six-month-old as a child.'

'My three children are well past that stage in their lives. In fact one of them has a baby daughter of her own. She certainly should know how to look after her. Isabel is a doctor in Houston. What's more, her husband is a paediatrician in the biggest hospital in Texas. So between them they should be able to give Sarah Louise the best possible start in life, I guess.' Mrs Price preened herself in such an ostentatious fashion that I could see Eleanor's face showing signs of instant irritation. My hope of overseas aid for the replacement of the safe and the carpet began to fade.

'Well, Mrs Price,' replied my wife, 'I am afraid my husband is no top paediatrician but I am a doctor like your daughter. Since my husband is a Vicar, between us we should be able to give our children the best possible start in life, the one to care for their souls and the other to care for their bodies. Would you like a cup of tea before you do your research into your ancestry?' To my great relief, the irony of my wife's reply passed unnoticed.

'I sure would like some of your excellent English tea but with no milk, please. I am allergic to milk.'

'Are you allergic to sugar?' inquired Eleanor.

'Only as far as my weight is concerned, Mrs Secombe. In other words, one teaspoonful of sugar would be just fine.'

When my wife went out to make the tea, I came into the conversation for the first time. 'How quaint, Vicar, that you are married to a doctor. Does she still practise her medicine? My daughter has given that up for the next four or five years at least, according to her schedule. They are planning another child in two years' time.'

'Eleanor has cut down on her commitments at the surgery and is a part-time practitioner at the moment. She is fortunate to have an excellent colleague whose work rate is phenomenal. However, she is hoping to be more active in the practice in a year or so's time. We have a very reliable nursemaid.'

'Do you have any other help in your Vicarage? It must be a great strain on your lovely wife to run a home and be involved in your parochial duties, if you'll pardon me saying so. I am an Episcopalian and I know how much our rector's wife has to do back home, being part of the prayer groups, the social committee and all that jazz.'

By now Mrs Susannah Price's inquisitional attitude was beginning to penetrate what Eleanor called my 'shell of clerical politeness'. I wondered how long it would be before I joined Eleanor in an aversion to our visitor.

'We have a treasure in Mrs Watkins, our part-time housekeeper, who is only too pleased to assist her part-time employee in running a well-organised household. Neither the parish nor its parish priest are the worse for the presence of a doctor in the Vicarage. I am sure the congregationers in Pontywen would testify to that.'

At this stage in the conversation my wife came into the room with a tea tray laden with our best china and a plate of biscuits. 'Your husband has just been telling me how well you have been able to schedule all your duties in what must be a very busy life. You are sure lucky to have such useful people at your elbow.'

As she put down the tray on the table, Eleanor replied,

'Without seeming to be big headed, that was not luck but was due to our unerring selective judgement. Would you like your tea weak, medium or strong?'

'Weak, please,' she replied. 'Anything more would upset my stomach. My daughter says I must keep a strict watch on my digestion. The slightest miscalculation could cause a reaction. I have a very delicate constitution.' My wife looked at me and I found it difficult to control an overwhelming desire to burst into mirth.

'It is a good thing you have come today and not a few days earlier, Mrs Price,' I said. 'Otherwise there would have been no registers for you to look at. We have had a daylight robbery at the church in the course of which the safe in the vestry and the carpet down the aisle were stolen.'

Her eyes and her mouth opened wide. 'You don't say! I would never have believed it in a place like this. We are used to hearing about robberies in the big cities in the USA though there are not many thefts in Austin. It is the capital city of Texas and very law abiding. So how come your registers are here for me to inspect?'

'Our local constable, commonly known as Will Book and Pencil, found the safe broken open and minus our valuable church silver but with the registers intact strewn alongside it. Fortunately the weather had been kind and no rain had fallen to damage the records. They are in my study, immaculate and ready for your perusal. You did not give me any details of your great-grandfather, otherwise I could have done some research before you arrived. In any case, it will not take long to trace your ancestry.'

'My!' she said. 'To think I could have come all this way to find out about my family roots and then to hear that everything had been destroyed. I sure am grateful to your Will Book and Pencil, as you call him, for his help. Do you think I could give him something to show my gratitude?'

'I am afraid,' I replied, 'that you would not be allowed to do that. As it would be said officially, it was all in the course of his duty. The great thing is that the church is once again in possession of its historic records, even if it is missing a safe at the moment. What is distressing is the loss of its priceless silver chalice, paten and flagon given to St Mary's by the forebears of Sir David Jones-Williams who were responsible for the building of this church. The carpet is easily replaced but not the silver.'

By the time I had finished my shameless, indirect appeal to the Texan pocket I received one of Eleanor's disapproving glances. However, the effect it had on Mrs Price was most encouraging. 'I hope you don't mind, Reverend Secombe,' she said, 'but I should sure like to help towards buying some of the best silver you can get for your new Communion set. Perhaps we could talk about it when we have had a look at your registers. I just can't wait to see them.'

After the tea and biscuits, I ushered our visitor into my study for the search into her Pontywen 'roots'.

'What a fine lot of books you have here,' she remarked. 'When do you get time to read in a busy life like yours?'

'I have not read them all by any means,' I replied. 'Most of them are here for reference rather than reading for pleasure. Now then, let's begin at the beginning, which is the best way to start, I suppose.' My attempt at humour passed unnoticed.

'I guess so,' she said. 'So where are the wonderful registers I have come to see. To think that I might be seeing the handwriting of my ancestors, perhaps.'

'Only if it is in a marriage register, of course, not if it is a baptism or a funeral.' Once again my schoolboy witticism failed to find the target. It was met with a dead-pan face.

'I guess not,' she replied.

'What was your maiden name, Mrs Price?' I enquired.

'My what?' she exclaimed.

'What was your name before you were married?'

'It is a strange name – Cadwallader.'

'That is not strange in Wales. It is another form of Caractacus, the famous King of the Celtic people in Mid Wales, a man who fought the Romans, a great hero of the Welsh.'

She looked at me in wide-eyed astonishment. 'You mean, I am descended from a famous King?'

'Well, it may be so. There must be thousands of Cadwalladers in Wales. The sexton at our sister church, St Illtyd's, is a Cadwallader. Perhaps you are related to him.'

'What do you mean by "sexton", Vicar?'

'He is the grave-digger.'

Her face fell. To be related to the equivalent of Hamlet was something wonderful, to be related to his grave-digger was not in the same category. It was evident that she had no intention of tracing any kinship with Tom but at least she could go back to Texas and trumpet the claim that buried in the distant past there was a royal ancestor.

'Well, what do you know?' she murmured. 'Wait till I get back home and tell the folks that I have royal blood in my veins.' When we found the first Cadwallader in the marriage registers it was in the year 1851. David William Cadwallader, collier, married Emily Elizabeth Davies, domestic servant. He was twenty-two years of age and she was seventeen. They had nine children recorded in the baptismal register and three recorded in the burial register in infancy. The fourth son, Albert Edward, baptised 20 May 1857, was the great-grandfather Susannah had come to trace. She clapped her hands as soon as she saw his name. David William died at the age of thirty-seven. Albert Edward, collier, married Agnes May Thomas, laundress, on 30 June 1880 and two years later set sail for Pennsylvania. Mrs Price recorded each entry meticulously in a notebook she had brought with her. By the time she had finished, her cup of happiness was running over. To discover her roots was one thing. To find they went back to Roman times and to a king was something else. I could imagine the éclat in Texas which would greet the revelation of her ancestry.

I took her for a tour of St Mary's, Pontywen, with its tasteless Victorian glass in the east window donated by the Jones-Williams family and with little else to offer. The bare stone floor of the aisle added to the uninspiring aspect of the church. However, Mrs Price seemed to find it attractive. 'I love these old churches,' she said. Back at the Vicarage, she drew a cheque book out of her handbag. 'This is in dollars,' she said, 'but I am sure your bank can translate it into your money. It is just a big thank you for all your kindness and help.' She proceeded to write out a cheque for a thousand dollars. 'Now, I think I had better go. I am due to meet my husband in Cardiff at six o'clock. I bet he hasn't had the luck I've had in finding my roots.'

As she waved goodbye, going down the drive in her taxi, Eleanor said, 'There goes your fairy godmother. Heaven knows, you worked hard enough to make her one. It reminded me of a story I once read about an American benefactor who had been responsible for the renovation of an ancient parish church. He came back for the re-dedication service and when the Vicar gave thanks during the service for "this unexpected succour", the bene-factor got up and walked out of the church in high indignation. I hope you will rephrase your thanksgiving if you are thinking of inviting her back for something similar.'

'I noticed you looking at me when I was letting her know how impoverished we were in Pontywen,' I replied.

'What is more I must admit to a feeling of guilt about my unwarranted imposition on her generosity.'

'Unwarranted imposition, my foot. I thought you exploited her kindness to the 'nth degree, Secombe. She may have been gullible but she was a good Christian lady who would help anyone in need. I happen to think you exaggerated the extent of St Mary's need far beyond what was required.'

'Before you say any more, my sweet,' I said, 'who sprayed her with sarcastic remarks? I know they went over her head, fortunately, but none the less they are hardly in accord with your description of her as a good Christian lady!'

'Touché,' admitted my wife. 'I suppose I should have made allowances for the Texan tendency to have the biggest and the best of everything and to show an inordinate amount of interest in other people's affairs. She is still a good Christian lady for all that.'

When I handed the cheque to David Vaughan-Jenkins, bank manager-cum-churchwarden, he whistled his astonishment at the amount. 'What with the money from the insurance plus this donation, St Mary's will be much better off than before the theft,' he remarked.

'That's exactly what my wife said,' I replied. 'She felt I had taken Mrs Susannah Price for a ride.'

'Knowing you, Vicar, I am sure you did no such thing, but whatever you did, I can tell you that the congregation will appreciate this boost to their finances. By the way, you will be pleased to know that we have purchased a twenty-four-inch television set, large enough to provide a view of the coronation for about a dozen members of the congregation in our lounge. I suppose that before long we had better begin to make out a list of viewers for the great day. What a headache that is going to be!'

This became apparent at the meeting of the coronation committee later that evening. After reports from those responsible for the various activities being organised as part of the celebrations, Idris the Milk raised the matter of the television audience. 'As you know, Vicar,' he said, 'we have nearly two hundred in the electoral roll of the parish and an average congregation per Sunday in the two churches of about a hundred and twenty. How on earth are we going to decide on who are going to watch the coronation in the respective houses which have got sets? I know we can all listen to the service on the wireless, but that's not the same as seeing it, is it?'

I sent up an urgent prayer for guidance and then launched into the deep. 'First of all, we must be very grateful to Mr and Mrs Vaughan-Jenkins and to Mr and Mrs Nicholls for their kindness in inviting members of the congregation to join them in viewing the great events of next 2 June. If the Vicarage was big enough I would gladly invite all our church people to come to see the coronation. As things are, that is impossible; I am sure that nobody thinks that they have a right to watch it on television. Many families will want to be together and listen to it on their wireless sets. Not all that long ago, they would not have been able to do that, so let's get matters in perspective.

'I think the emphasis must be on the family. Talking of rights, the children have as much right to be in on the occasion as the grown ups. It is *their* future which will be bound up with what is going to happen on Coronation Day. As far as I can make out, there will be provision for about fifty people at most to view the proceedings, so let me put it this way, how many of the congregation would be willing to leave their families to come and watch it without their children?'

There was what might be termed a pregnant pause as the committee considered my emphasis on the family. Inevitably it was Idris who was the first to speak. 'Thank you, Vicar, for bringing us back to earth. Isn't it strange how selfish we can become. Never mind the kids, let's get in on the act ourselves.'

Then David Vaughan-Jenkins was on his feet. 'As one who is to be host to twelve viewers, I echo the Vicar's sentiment in wishing that I could give hospitality to ten times that number. As that is impossible, might I suggest that we put up a list in both of the churches, limiting the number of – er – applicants, as it were, to two from each family. Further, might I suggest that the Vicar writes an article in next month's magazine based on what he has said here tonight.' This was greeted with a number of grunted 'Hear! Hear!s' and silence from the rest of the congregation. It was obvious that the advent of television in Pontywen was going to sow the seeds of discontent in our two churches.

'Thank you for those suggestions, Mr Vaughan-Jenkins,' I said. 'I shall be writing about the televising of the coronation in any case. As for the placing of a list on the noticeboard of each church, I think that is an excellent idea. However, I think it would be wise to delay that until I have written my article in the magazine and addressed both congregations on the matter. In the meanwhile let us get on with our preparations for the celebrations after the coronation is over. There is more than enough to keep us occupied, what with organising the tea in the church hall, the purchase of mugs for the children, the Punch and Judy show, the concert, the dance and so on. So let's get our priorities right.'

When I went back to the Vicarage and told Eleanor of what had happened, she said. 'What a devious man you are! Earlier today you extracted a thousand dollars from the Texan lady and now you have used the children as pawns in your attempt to avoid blood letting over the television problem – but I must say, Frederick, I take my hat off to you. I don't think any of the clergy in this neck of the wood would have been able to rise to the occasion like you.' She kissed me lightly on the cheek. 'Now then, my dear, you have another problem to solve. While you were engaged in your tactical manoeuvres in the church hall, I had a telephone call from our mutual friend and pain in the neck, Charles Wentworth-Baxter. He is begging you to go to Bronwen and plead on his behalf for her return to the matrimonial home. I told him in no uncertain terms what I thought of him and that he had a nerve to ask you to intervene in what is essentially their own private affair. According to him he has turned over a new leaf. I told him he had turned over so many new leaves that he has gone through the whole book already. He is terrified that the Bishop will get to hear of what has happened and that he will be suspended from the living. I said I would tell you about his call when you came in.'

'Oh, no!' I exclaimed.

'Oh, yes!' she replied.

'I can't possibly talk to him tonight; my head is in a whirl. How can I go to that poor girl and ask her to return to a husband who has physically abused her and even ill treated one of his children. I'll sleep on it and give him a ring in the morning.' I put my arms around her and hugged her.

'I think you are being very wise, my love,' she said. 'Let him stew in his own juice until the morning. I hope he doesn't have a single minute's sleep. He doesn't deserve a second, let alone a minute.'

No sooner had she said that than the telephone rang. 'Sorry, Fred,' murmured my wife, 'but it's that man again.'

I picked up the receiver. 'Hello!' I snapped.

'Fred, thank God it's you. Has Eleanor told you I phoned?' He sounded like a man at the end of his tether. His voice was shrill and unnatural.

'She has indeed, Charles. I have only just come in from a committee meeting.'

Before I could say anything more he broke down and began wailing. 'I'm sorry, Fred. I've been a fool, a big fool. I don't deserve her, she's far too good for me. If she doesn't come back I'll do away with myself. I will, I tell you that. It's only now I realise how much I love her and how much I have hurt her.'

'Hurt her,' I shouted. 'You have hurt her body as well as her soul. Now you want me to ask her back to be hurt all over again. Look, Charles. How much is this repentance due to your fear that the Bishop will have it in for you if he finds out what you have done to her. How much is due to genuine regret that you could have been such a callous brute.'

The wailing continued, 'I know I have been beastly to her but I miss her so much as well as the children.'

'They have only been away for a day or so, Charles.

You haven't had time to miss her much and if you think I am going to her mother's place to ask her to come back to you, you are very much mistaken. You go and do it for yourself. I have done enough hauling you out of trouble in the past. It's time that you stood on your own two feet. Goodnight.' I slammed the phone down.

'Good for you,' said Eleanor. 'Let's get to bed.'

We went to bed but I could not sleep; my mind was in a turmoil. I kept thinking of my former curate's threats to do away with himself. If he did that, would I be partly to blame because I refused to help him, I asked myself. When I did sleep, I was plagued with dreams, culminating with me finding Charles with his head in a gas oven. I awoke in a cold sweat and sat up suddenly, waking Eleanor in the process.

'What's the matter, love?' she asked drowsily.

'I've just had a horrible dream. I found Charles with his head in a gas oven.'

'No such luck,' she replied and turned over on her side.

The dream was so vivid that I could not get back to sleep. I was glad when the day dawned and Eleanor got up to feed the baby. As she sat beside me in bed cradling Elspeth in her arms, she said, 'You've had a disturbed night.'

'I can't get Charles out of my mind after that awful dream,' I replied.

'What dream?' she asked.

'I told you that I had found him with his head in a gas oven and you said "No such luck" and went back to sleep.'

'I don't remember that, love. Anyway they are still my sentiments. Bronwen and the kids would be far better off without him. That man is a menace. He is one leopard who will never change his spots. If you are worried about the gas oven dream, don't forget they haven't any gas in Penglais. Secondly, if they did Charles would bungle his suicide attempt. Thirdly, he would never have the nerve to do anything of that nature anyway. He likes his own life too much to do that. You have wasted some precious sleep, Frederick. What about a nice cup of tea, then? I don't see why the baby should be the only one to get some light refreshment.'

When I went across to the church to open up for morning service I was surprised to see Miss Harding, the headmistress of the Infant School in Pontywen. A large lady, in height and weight, with a booming voice, she was a member of the congregation at St Padarn's. As she was not a regular worshipper there her presence at daily Matins in the church which normally consisted of a dialogue between Vicar and Curate was unexpected, to say the least. She was in earnest conversation with Emlyn Howells who looked relieved to see me coming up the path. Her powerful contralto tones drowned the clergy's contribution to the general confession and the Lord's Prayer. When we came to the psalms appointed for the morning, her recital of the alternate verses proceeded at a gallop, leaving Emlyn a poor second both in pace and in volume. After the service she was waiting outside as Emlyn and I came from the vestry door. 'Are you coming my way, Mr Howells?' she inquired in an affectedly coy fashion.

'I am afraid Mr Howells has to come to the Vicarage for our daily parish strategy meeting, Miss Harding,' I said.

'See you Sunday, Mr Howells,' she cooed loudly and made her ungainly way towards the lych gate.

'Daily parish strategy meeting,' said my curate. 'That's a new one, but thank you all the same for the deliverance. Miss Virginia Harding is becoming a big nuisance, I can assure you.'

'I could see that,' I replied. 'Well, do you want to come in for a cup of coffee and a dose of strategy or would you rather get straight back home?'

'I think a cup of coffee would be very welcome, Vicar, and perhaps a chat about the big nuisance would be in order. I have been meaning to talk to you about her for some time. Your advice on the subject will be as welcome as the coffee, believe me.'

As we sat drinking coffee, I said to Emlyn, 'I thought it strange to see Miss Harding there this morning. It's not as if she were a regular worshipper at St Padarn's.'

'Oh, but she is now,' he replied. 'She is there at every service I take and always hangs around to speak to me afterwards. She has insisted on lending me books I don't want and on bringing them round to my house. If I ask for volunteers for any function at St Padarn's she is always first in the queue. The trouble is that the congregation have noticed this and are beginning to assume that there is some relationship between us. God forbid! The last thing I want is any kind of relationship with that lady. She terrifies me, as I believe she does her pupils.'

'Well, Emlyn,' I said, 'sooner or later you will have to be very frank with her and make it plain that you have no interest in her whatsoever. You are such a tolerant person that you will find it difficult to be rude – but rude you will have to be, otherwise she will make your life a misery. She is such an overpowering person. No wonder she has "Jumbo" as her nickname.'

He began to laugh. 'That's very unkind but very appropriate, I'm afraid. I have never known such a clumsy person. She has knocked over my standard lamp and broken two wine glasses on the few occasions she has been at my place.'

'All the more fool you for inviting her in,' I told him. 'From now on, if she comes with a book, keep her standing on the doorstep. If she hangs around after service find a way of going out by the vestry door. She will soon get the message. The sooner the better, Emlyn. Miss Harding is a formidable lady, so don't delay.'

Eleanor was highly amused when I told her about the Harding obsession with the curate. 'She is at least twenty years older than Emlyn,' she said. 'Perhaps you could help by paying a visit to the Infant School and inventing a fiancée for the poor man to get him out of her clutches. Tell her that his young lady is very attractive and has not been able to visit Pontywen yet because she lives in the Shetland Isles.'

'You accused me yesterday of being devious in my dealings with Mrs Susannah Price,' I replied. 'At least I did not tell lies. Now you are inciting me to tell whoppers of which Baron Munchausen would be proud. I take it that you are not being serious. In any case, if he takes my advice, I don't think he will be troubled any further.'

'We'll see,' she said and proceeded to change the baby's napkin. 'At least if they did get married, she would not have to be lumbered with this routine.'

Before she could say anything further on the unlikely possibility of Miss Harding becoming Mrs Howells, the telephone rang. It was the lady in question. 'Vicar!' her voice had the resonance of a town crier.

'Ah, Miss Harding,' I said.

'How did you recognise my voice so instantly? I am most impressed,' she boomed.

'You have one of those voices which are unmistakable. Good to see you at Matins this morning. What can I do for you?'

'Well, Vicar, I have been thinking of ways in which those children in my school who have no connection with organised Christianity could at least be in touch with the clergy in this town. The most obvious way is to get the clergy into the school. So I have been wondering if you would allow the Reverend Emlyn Howells to come in occasionally and speak to the children. He has a rare gift for speaking to the age groups we have here. I am sure that my pupils would benefit enormously and, who knows, the church as well.'

I sent up an arrow prayer for the second time in less than twenty-four hours. 'If you don't mind me saying so, Miss Harding, I think it would be better if the Vicar came rather than the curate. He is the persona of the parish. Curates come and go but the incumbent is more or less a permanent fixture. I, too, like talking to children. All the more so since I have a young son myself. So, if you can put up with me, I shall be pleased to come whenever you invite me.'

There was a long silence at the other end of the phone. When she spoke, the boom gave way to a more moderate but acid tone. 'As you please, Vicar. I just thought it would be a useful experience for Mr Howells. I shall be in touch with you.'

After the abrupt ending to the conversation, Eleanor came into the study. 'Miss Harding?' she inquired.

I told her of the way in which I had rescued poor Emlyn Howells from her clutches once again. 'She said that it would have been a useful experience for the curate,' I added.

'Useful for her, she meant,' my wife replied.

8

A red-headed leprechaun with vivid blue eyes and a strong Belfast accent stood on my doorstep later that morning. 'My apologies, Vicar, for coming uninvited,' he said, 'but as I was in the neighbourhood I thought I would take the opportunity to call on you with a proposition. Joe McNally, Catholic priest at Abergelly. How do you do?' He put out his hand and held mine firmly, looking me in the eye whilst doing so.

'Come on in, Father. I am very pleased to meet you.' I led him into my study. He looked around at my books and expressed his approval.

'Quite a good library you have here. More than enough to keep you occupied. I am afraid mine is very limited in comparison, but there you are, perhaps I spend too much time outside and not enough indoors.'

'The same goes for me,' I said. 'Don't be misled by the quantity of books. I just use them to make an impression on my Bishop. Now would you like a cup of coffee? I am afraid it is too early in the day to offer you whisky.'

'My dear Vicar, it is never too early in the day to offer me a whisky – that is, if you have any available.'

As we sat drinking the aqua vitae he broached the subject of his proposition. 'There are quite a few Catholics in Pontywen – not enough to warrant the building of a church, you know. Still, there are sufficient to have their own opportunity to worship. Abergelly is a fair distance away and on a Sunday morning the bus service is non existent, so it is. I was wondering whether you would be prepared to allow us the use of your altar at St Padarn's after your Mass is finished. We would give you a reasonable amount of money for that, of course. I know it sounds like a piece of impertinence on our part but I can tell you that your co-operation would be appreciated, so it would be.'

'Well, Father McNally, I must confess that this is an unusual request. As far as I am concerned I shall be only too pleased to allow you to worship in St Padarn's. However, I shall have to ask the Bishop's permission and I will have to get the consent of the Parochial Church Council. Once this is done, there is no reason why you should not have your Mass at St Padarn's.'

A broad smile spread over the face of Father Joe McNally. 'Now that's what I call a really Christian attitude. I am afraid we give the impression that we are the only authorised children of God. I don't know whether you have heard the story of someone who was taken up to heaven to do a kind of Cook's tour. He was met by an angel guide who led him first of all to a crowd of people who were singing Sankey and Moody hymns lustily. "They are the Pentecostals," he said. Then he led him to a small group who were sitting in silence and contemplating their navels. "That's the Quakers," he explained. After that they moved on to another group of boys and men who were singing the psalms so beautifully that the visitor to heaven was moved to tears. "That's the Church of England," the angel said. Then he was taken to another part of heaven which was surrounded by a big wall. "Where are we now?" he asked his guide. The angel said to him, "Keep your voice down. These are the Roman Catholics. They think they are the only people up here." I can tell you, Vicar, that there are some of us who are only too willing to acknowledge the presence of other workers in the Lord's vineyard and that we have not the monopoly of the faith.'

'How big a congregation would you expect at the altar?' I asked.

He looked at the ceiling and made a mental calculation. 'About forty or fifty, I should say, with the Italian element predominating. You know, I sometimes think that there are more Italians in the valleys than there are in Rome. Then there are a few Murphys and Ryans who have found their way to Pontywen. A few of my colleagues have started to learn Welsh. I have told them that they are wasting their sweetness on the desert air. The natives of the valleys know as much about their mother tongue as they would about Swahili, excepting their National Anthem, of course. They've got to know about that to sing their team to victory at Cardiff Arms Park, so they have.'

'By the way,' I said, 'do you know Father Eamon McCarthy who was a curate at St Bernadette's in Swansea in the early nineteen forties? I expect he has left there by now but I was very friendly with him. We both used to run soccer teams in the youth league and his church was just down the road from mine. On many occasions, we used to have chats about ecumenical relations. He was prepared to accept the Anglicans but drew the line at any other denomination.'

'Would you believe it? I know him quite well. He has left Swansea and he has gone to his own church in

Cardiff – Our Lady of the Sea. You must pay him a visit one day. Eamon comes from my part of Belfast and I remember him as just a wee lad who served at the altar in my home church. Father Francis, the parish priest, thought the world of him. It is a small world, that it is.' Our conversation continued for another half hour or so by the end of which we had arrived at Christian name terms and I had promised to let him know in a week's time whether his flock could worship in St Padarn's. 'You must come down and have a meal at my place. My housekeeper is a very good cook and I keep an excellent cellar.'

I debated with myself whether I should write to the Bishop or telephone him. In view of the fact that I had promised to let Joe know within a week about the Bishop and the Parochial Church Council's response I decided to ring his lordship immediately. His secretary answered.

'Would you mind delaying your call for another quarter of an hour, shall we say? The Bishop has someone with him at the moment. I shall tell him you have phoned.'

I spent the next quarter of an hour ruminating about possible opponents to the proposition in the Parochial Church Council. Ezekiel Evans, the lay reader, was a certainty. Bertie Owen was another. On the other hand such an alliance would be sufficient to persuade the rest of the Council to vote in favour, just to spite them. My speculation was ended abruptly by the telephone bell. It was the Bishop inquiring about the purpose of my call.

'Can you make it short, Vicar? I have to go out very soon.'

'It is a somewhat unusual request, my lord.'

'Nothing to do with Charles Wentworth-Baxter, I trust.'

'Not at all, the Roman Catholic priest at Abergelly has asked me whether I would be prepared to let him have the use of the altar at St Padarn's once a Sunday after the morning service was over. Apparently he has between forty and fifty worshippers in Pontywen who are more or less cut off because of the poor bus service on Sundays. He is prepared to make a regular payment to be agreed if permission is granted. I told him I would have to consult you first and also the Parochial Church Council.'

'I see,' said his lordship. I waited quite a while before he spoke again.

'As you say, it is an unusual request. I have heard of it done in a few English dioceses but this is the first occasion I have been asked to give permission for such an arrangement in this diocese. Well, if the Parochial Church Council are agreeable, I would be willing to allow it for an experimental period of twelve months. Should everything be congenial after such a trial, then I would probably be prepared to let the agreement go on indefinitely.'

'Thank you very much, my lord,' I replied.

'Oh, by the way, what has happened about Wentworth-Baxter's request to serve as an extra unpaid curate?' he inquired. Obviously he had heard nothing of Charles's matrimonial troubles about which I thought it wise to be silent.

'When I gave him a list of what I would require him to do if he came to Pontywen, he decided he would rather stay in his own parish. I had no need to consult the Parochial Church Council. All he wanted was an excuse to escape from Penglais.'

'Typical of that young man,' said the Bishop. 'Sometimes I wonder what will become of him. I am afraid he has no sense of vocation. I think he must have been railroaded into the ministry by his father who insisted that his one and only son should follow in his footsteps. There have been many such cases. Inevitably they result in unfortunate clerical misfits. Well, I must go now, Vicar. I hope the experimental cooperation with the Roman Catholic Church proves more fruitful than the Wentworth-Baxter proposition.'

When Eleanor came in after one of her occasional morning surgeries, I told her of my visit by Father Joe McNally and then of my conversation with the Bishop. 'Well, Frederick,' she said, 'I am afraid the Wentworth-Baxter saga continues to unfold. Earlier this morning I had a phone call from Bronwen. She had rung the Vicarage but could not get a reply.'

'That must have been when I went to get my newspaper,' I replied. 'Marlene had taken the children out and evidently Mrs Watkins either did not hear the phone or, more likely, chose to ignore it and get on with her work.'

'Whatever the reason, that time there was no reply, and she rang the surgery. It seems that Charles appeared at her parent's house, banging on the door and demanding to see his wife and children. Fortunately Bronwen's father was working afternoons and was at home. Apparently he took Charles apart and told him that he was lucky not to be in a police court that morning. He warned him that if ever he assaulted his daughter again, he would beat the daylights out of him. Now the silly girl has decided to go back for a trial period. She has told him that if there is any more violence she will leave him for good. I think she is on a hiding to nothing, if you will excuse the dreadful pun. Anyway, I have told her that I will keep a close eye on her and that she must ring me immediately if she gets any more trouble from her stupid spouse.'

That afternoon I had been invited to speak at the weekly old-age pensioners' meeting which was held at the Miners' Welfare Hall. The Pontywen building was modest, compared with the grandiose complex at Abergelly, with its pillared frontage, large theatre, and several reception facilities. Its main feature was an excellent library, little used nowadays, according to Idris the Milk.

'Most of the miners go to the clubs or to Abergelly,' he told me. 'It's only the old-age pensioners that keep it going. A sign of the times, that's what it is. Once upon a time they used to have debates there and have really good speakers. Now it's the clubs that get the numbers with the booze and the so-called entertainment. There's so much money about that the wives want to be in on the act. You can't blame them, I suppose. What's good for the goose is good for the gander.'

I was due to be there at three o'clock. I arrived at five minutes to three, to find the committee room which was used as their meeting place full of noisy chattering elderly people, all seated on uncomfortable tubular chairs. There was an ancient wooden table in front of the gathering, out of place with the rest of the furniture. Behind it were three chairs of the tubular variety, two occupied and the other waiting to seat me. The Chairman, Dan Evans, stood up to shake my hand and to welcome me.

'Well, Vicar, it's a pleasure to see you. We are looking forward to your address. If you don't mind, we have some business to attend to before you begin to speak. Take a seat and make yourself comfortable.'

I would defy anyone to make himself comfortable on a piece of plastic held together by aluminium supports. I did my best.

On the other side of Dan, was the secretary, Miss Mabel Jones, retired schoolteacher and an active citizen of Pontywen, prominent in the Townswomen's Guild and local Labour Party. She raised her head from a perusal of the opened minute book and murmured a greeting, after which she turned over the page to read the other side. There was a tumbler of water in front of me, beside a lectern. Evidently they expected a lengthy address.

'Now then,' said the Chairman. 'First of all, let's welcome our speaker, no stranger to you all by any means. He has been in Pontywen for about eight years now. I think I am right.' He turned to me and I nodded. 'There you are, eight years. He must like us a lot to be here for such a length of time. Anyway, during that time he has done much. None of us will forget how he has stood up for the miners and what's more what his wife did for them in that terrible accident which took so many lives.' There was spontaneous applause at this point. 'Anyway let's get down to business. Shall we have the minutes of the last meeting, Miss Jones.' She adjusted her spectacles, cleared her throat and declared rather than read the minutes. It was an impressive performance worthy of a better text than a minute book.

'Matters arising?' asked the Chairman. There were several matters arising and it was half past three before I was called upon to address the meeting. 'Mr Chairman,' I began, 'thank you for your kind words earlier on. Yes, I have always had a great admiration for the miners. Any man who earns his living by crawling about in the bowels of the earth inhaling coal dust and risking life and limb is worthy of admiration. The history of coal mining in this country is littered with examples of shameless exploitation not only of men but women and children who rarely saw daylight and were paid a pittance. When I took my history degree I chose as my special subject Anthony Ashley Cooper, the seventh Earl of Shaftesbury, who devoted his political life to releasing women and children from their slavery in the mines, fighting the vested interests of the coal magnates.' As I proceeded to describe in detail the life of the noble lord from his early years to his death as an old man, I could see many pairs of eyes glazed over and I could hear many sighs from around the room. It was when the coughing began that I decided that enough was enough and I brought my lecture to an abrupt end. There was half-hearted applause. Then the Chairman rose to speak.

'Thank you for your talk about Lord Shaftesbury, Vicar. By a strange coincidence we had another talk about him a fortnight ago from Professor Tudor Matthews. So it's like what you say when you read the banns, it's for the second time of asking. You weren't to know that, were you? That's life, I suppose. Are there any questions for our speaker?' It seemed that no one wanted to ask a question. Evidently they had used up their quota of questions on Lord Shaftesbury a fortnight ago. Then suddenly an old man with a scarf tucked into his jacket spoke from his seat at the back of the room.

'Mr Chairman,' he breathed in bronchitic fashion, 'would the speaker like to tell us why he is on the side of the miners when he has never seen the inside of a coal mine and his bishops at the time of Lord Shaftesbury were supporting the coal owners in the House of Lords while the Earl as a Christian was trying to rescue the poor women and children from a life of slavery. Either he is a hypocrite or he is in the wrong job. I don't seem to hear of the bishops today defending the miners.'

I was so confused by the question that I did not know where to begin the answer, back in the nineteenth century or in the nineteen fifties. I decided to plump for the present day.

'You ask why I am on the side of the miners. Well, first of all, I am of working-class origins. I was brought up on a council estate in the docks district of Swansea. The people where I lived were steelworkers, dockers and trawler men. The steelworkers and the trawler men had to face risks in their employment. I may not have been inside the heat and dust of a steelworks or on a trawler facing the hazards of the Bristol Channel or the Irish Sea, but I could imagine what they had to face. Once I went out into Swansea Bay with a docker who lived a few doors away from us. I think I was about twelve at the time. I was thrilled to be going out in a rowing boat with him. After half an hour when we were away from the shelter of the harbour I was violently sick. I had to watch him eat the sandwiches my mother had prepared for me. It was like Chinese torture. I did not stop being sick until we reached dry land. Another day I went to the steelworks and felt suffocated in the heat and the dust. I don't have to go down the mines to realise what the miners have to endure. I heard enough from my wife when she came back from that terrible disaster to know the conditions under which they have to work. As for the bishops in the time of Lord Shaftesbury, they were the creatures of their own environment, their episcopal palaces and their pleasant pastures. They were blind to the realities of coal mining. I am not and I am no hypocrite, I can assure you.'

I spoke with such vehemence that my listeners were moved to give me a hand clap, which was deafening in comparison with my earlier reception. The man with the scarf sat unmoved. 'After that', said the Chairman, 'I think we had better have our tea and biscuits.'

As we sat drinking our tea Dan Evans commented, 'I tell you what, your answer to Llew Jones was better than Professor Matthews's and your lecture rolled into one. You spoke with such conviction that you made us feel you were one of us and not one of them. What more can you ask of a Vicar than that? As for Llew, unless you had spent years in a pit, he would never accept you as one of us.'

The following Monday evening I had to preside at the hastily convened Parochial Church Council meeting to discuss the possible use of St Padarn's altar by Father Joe McNally. I had mentioned the purpose of the special session to Idris the Milk and Charlie Hughes, the two churchwardens, after the service on Sunday. 'That's a turn up for the book,' said Idris, 'to have the Roman Catholics wanting to worship in our church. I think it's marvellous.' It took Charlie, who was now deafer than ever, at least a couple of minutes adjusting his hearing aid to understand the reason for the meeting.

'What about the Roman Catholics, Vicar? They want to buy our church. Never.'

'No, Charlie, they would like to rent our church to have their own service after we have had ours.'

'Oh, that's different. You mean that they are going to pay us something each Sunday. We could do with the money, that's certain. Mind, you'll have to watch them to see they pay every Sunday.' Charlie was in charge of counting the collection.

Before the meeting began, I could see Ezekiel Evans and Bertie Owen working in tandem to persuade members of the Council to reject the proposition, as I had foreseen. The more they proceeded to browbeat their visitors the more convinced I became that this unholy alliance would ensure that the motion to accept the proposition would be passed with only two voting against. When the minutes of the last meeting had been read and confirmed I re-counted the details of my meeting with Father McNally. 'I can only say,' I went on, 'that I was most impressed by his breadth of vision. He is a Catholic in the true sense of the word, broadminded and tolerant. I am positive that if we allow them to share the use of the altar in St Padarn's it will be a significant advance in ecumenical relations in this valley. The Bishop is quite prepared to give his blessing to the enterprise for an experimental period of twelve months and then to extend it indefinitely if it proves successful.'

Immediately Ezekiel Evans was on his feet, his face flushed with righteous indignation. 'H'is this the thin h'edge h'of the wedge? Can't you see that 'e is 'oping to h'attract members of our congregation who might stay on to see 'ow 'e conducts 'is service? 'E's only pretending to be broadminded. They h'intend to take over h'our church one of these days, believe me. H'as far h'as they are concerned, we are the h'infidels in 'is eyes. H'I can't h'understand why our Bishop 'as been bamboozled, let alone you, Vicar.'

Next Bertie Owen jumped up. 'I would like to support what Mr Evans has said. For years, in fact, all my life, the Roman Catholics have despised us. They don't even recognise weddings that take place in our churches. Now, suddenly, they want to take over one of our buildings for their own purpose. Why haven't they asked you, Vicar, if they could have the parish church instead of St Padarn's? How would you like to have the stink of incense there instead of us suffering it in our little church? I tell you what, if the Council vote for this to go ahead, they'll need to have their heads read.'

It was the turn of Idris the Milk to say his piece. 'Well, Vicar, if you listen to what Ezekiel and Bertie have been saying, it seems that the end of the world has come because we are doing our fellow Christians an act of kindness. There are Roman Catholics in Pontywen who can't get down to Abergelly for Mass, because the bus service on Sundays is hopeless. Are we going to deny them the right to have Communion because we are small-minded? If you are worried about the stink of incense, Bertie, as you put it, you needn't be because, by the time Sunday comes around once again, the church will have been cleaned and aired. What's more, if I may say so, you have been very insulting to the rest of us in the Council by saying that we need to have our heads read if we don't agree with you. The boot is on the other foot.'

'And if the cap fits, wear it,' murmured David Vaughan-Jenkins, who was at my side. Charlie Hughes was having trouble with his hearing aid, which had been whistling ever since the meeting began. Now he stood up to make his contribution.

'I didn't hear much of what has been said, my battery has been going, but I would like to say this. I'm all for the Roman Catholics being able to rent our church. The collections have not been all that great these past few months and every little bit helps, as you know. The sooner they start the better, as far as I am concerned.' He sat down and switched off his hearing aid to save his battery.

Ten minutes later the Council had made their decision, to accept the proposition, with only two votes against. When the meeting was over, Emlyn Howells asked if he could have a word with me after Matins next morning. 'Why not come back to the Vicarage now for a cup of coffee?' I suggested. He accepted the invitation gladly. He had been looking glum throughout the proceedings. Normally he would have been enjoying the spectacle of Ezekiel and Bertie making fools of themselves.

When we sat down to drink the coffee in my study, he explained his desire to 'have a word'. 'It's that woman, Harding,' he said, with more than a hint of desperation in his voice. 'I think I am a tolerant bloke, but my limit of tolerance has reached breaking point. I am sorry I ever suggested that the PCC might agree to me having a phone. Ever since it was installed a month ago and the number was printed in the church magazine, she has been driving me crazy with her incessant ringing. Whenever I answer, she has the most implausible excuse for the call. During this last week or two she has developed another technique. The phone rings. I pick it up and say my number, then the dialler puts down the phone. It is getting to the stage where it is playing on my mind. I have even had one of those calls at two o'clock in the morning. I have no proof that it is she but I am positive that it is. I don't know whether you can do anything to help, Vicar. You have helped quite a lot already with keeping her away from me. This is a different problem altogether. I have been very curt to her when she calls. It seems to have no effect. Next day she is back on the phone. I suppose sooner or later I shall have to cut her off as soon as she speaks, rude as it may be. Even that will not end these anonymous calls.'

'Let's go in the lounge and talk to Eleanor to see if she has any suggestions to make. You can have a whisky as well to soothe your shattered nerves. Tell Eleanor about your phone calls while I go to the kitchen for some aqua vitae,' I said.

'Not from the tap, I hope, dear,' she called as I went down the passage. By the time I returned with a bottle and a jug of water, Emlyn was coming to the end of his tale of woe.

'That two o'clock ring was the last straw.'

'I can see that,' my wife replied. 'You could go ex-directory, of course, but that would be the last straw in another sense, since you have had the phone put in for your parish work. I suppose you could use that device as a temporary measure. Better still would be a direct confrontation with the old battleaxe in the course of which you could warn her not to pester you any more, otherwise you will have to take some kind of legal action. I should think that would frighten her off. If it doesn't, then you can go to a solicitor and get an injunction. I am sorry, Emlyn, but unless you do something drastic she will not let go! She is at the time of life when women are subject to obsessional fantasies as well as hot flushes. As a stranded spinster left behind by the tides of the passing years, she sees you as her last chance of happiness.'

The prospect of a face-to-face encounter with the formidable Virginia Harding did nothing to lift the gloom which had enveloped my curate. By the time he left the Vicarage he looked even more miserable than when he came in. When I returned to the lounge, Eleanor said, 'It is a pity that he is such a nice man. I suppose it is one of the tragedies of life that people like Emlyn seem to attract such man-eating types as "Jumbo" Harding. Well, either he braces himself for the fray or he has a nervous breakdown.'

'I haven't told you about my talk to the old-age pensioners, have I?' I asked.

'No, you haven't. If you will arrange to do these things while I am out on my rounds, that's your fault, Frederick. Why, did anything interesting happen? One more nightcap before I listen to your account.' She poured us both a generous refill.

'Well, I decided to give them my talk on Lord Shaftesbury, which has gone down well, as you know, on several occasions. I couldn't understand why my riveting *tour de force* was leaving them stone cold. As a matter of fact, there was a fair amount of coughing and half-closed eyes. So I finished as quickly as I could. When Dan Evans got up to speak, the reason became obvious. A fortnight ago Professor Tudor Matthews from Cardiff University had also given a talk on Anthony Ashley Cooper. Then an old man with a scarf round his neck accused me of being a hypocrite to be on the side of the miners when all the bishops at the time of Shaftesbury were supporters of the coal owners and that I myself had never been down a coal mine. Apparently his name was Llew Jones. I must say he sounded full of dust. His voice and his breathing showed he must have spent his life underground.'

She began to laugh uproariously. 'Llew Jones is a patient of mine. Otherwise known as Llew the Scarf. He is a pain in the neck. That cough and his breathing are the product of heavy smoking. He never worked underground. He was employed as winder at the pit head.'

9

Next morning I rang Father McNally to inform him that the Bishop and the Parochial Church Council had agreed to an experimental period of one year's use of the altar at St Padarn's for his Sunday Mass in Pontywen.

His response was one of profuse gratitude. 'How wonderful! My dear Fred, you're a miracle worker, that's what you are. Between me and that old gate post they talk about, I thought that your bishop would have put his episcopal foot down, that I did. Now then, would you like to come over to the presbytery and work out the details over a nice little meal and some lubricant for the throat?' We agreed that we would meet in a week's time. Before he rang off, he said, 'Oh, by the way, would you like to bring a music copy of *Hymns Ancient and Modern* with you? I think your hymns are much better than ours, and I have quite a reasonable piano here. We can have a *cymanfa ganu* of our own.' Considering that he had said in our first conversation that he saw no point in his colleagues learning Welsh, at least he knew the Welsh for a singing get-together.

'I shall look forward to that,' I said. 'I hope your housekeeper can sing soprano. Then we can sing parts.'

'She's tone deaf,' he replied, 'but I tell you this, she can certainly cook and that's what matters in a housekeeper.'

That afternoon, it was my turn to do the hospital visiting. How times had changed since I first came to

Pontywen as a curate. Then I was terrified of the sisters and even more of entering the women's wards. Now, with a wife who was a doctor, I was treated with the utmost respect both by patients and staff. My first visit was to old Mr Tapscott who had been taken into hospital, suffering from incessant hiccups. When I went into the ward, he was sitting up in bed, looking a picture of health reading the *Daily Herald*. He was in his seventies and married to a wife some thirty years younger. They had a fourteen-year-old daughter who had been confirmed recently.

'How are you feeling, Mr Tapscott?' I asked.

The response was a hiccup. 'Apart from these b-blasted things I am fine.' There followed another 'blasted thing'. He looked around the ward furtively and then turned to me, lowering his voice. 'They say they don't know what's causing it (hiccup). I think it's what they're doing (hiccup) to the water. You know, every Tuesday (hiccup) they put that distemper in our taps. Before long there'll be lots of people in bed like (hiccup) me. I don't know whether Doctor (hiccup) Secombe can do anything to stop it before it's (hiccup) too late.'

'I'll have a word with her when I get home,' I replied, 'but I shouldn't think it's the water, it's more likely to be you and your digestive system.'

Our conversation continued for a few more minutes about the chlorination of the water supply, which he still insisted was responsible for his hiccups. I had gone to see old man Tapscott as a soft option before being confronted with the formidable Edwina Davies in the Princess Royal ward. After listening to an endless series of hiccups, I

began to wonder if any other hospital visit could be more
insufferable. I should have known better.

As soon as I entered the ward, I met Sister Mary
Rogers who was striding towards the door in high dudgeon. 'Well, Vicar,' she said, speaking through the corner
of her mouth, 'she's all yours and may the best man win
because I can't.'

There was no missing Edwina. She was in the bottom
bed on the left. She was waving and shouting 'Vicar!'
at the same time. 'Where have you been?' she demanded when I reached her. 'I thought you had left the
parish.'

'Now, come on, Mrs Davies,' I replied. 'I was here a
fortnight ago and Mr Howells was here last week.'

'All I can say', she replied, 'is that it seems donkey's

years since you were here last. You don't know what it's like to be stuck here in this place – nobody to talk to. All these old girls around here have got their heads stuck under the bedclothes, except when they're having their meals. I can't read because I need new glasses. My eyesight's getting worse. I think it's got a lot worse since I've been in here. The light is terrible. I tell you what, I'll be glad to get out of here. They say it will be another three weeks at least before they will let me get up. The last time I was in I was out of bed much earlier. It's this new specialist. He's a real dictator! "I know what's best for you, Miss Davies," he said. "So you obey my instructions and what's more you obey them when you go home. Otherwise you'll be a cripple for the rest of your life. If you had been a wise woman, you would not have been in here in the first place. Doing the sailor's hornpipe with a hip like yours. You should have known better." How was I to know I was going to dislocate my hip? I've been doing the hornpipe ever since I was a kid. Who does he think he is, the young whipper snapper? He is not long out of his nappies. You'd think he'd have more respect for his elders. I began to wish that she had caught distemper from the water like Mr Tapscott. At least it would have staunched the torrent of words. As she paused for breath, I ventured a remark. 'I'm sure that he must have respect for you, Mrs Davies. I am told that Mr Michael is one of the finest hip specialists in South Wales. So it would be just as well to listen to what he says.'

Almost before I could finish my last sentence, she continued her monologue, as if she had not heard a single word I had said. 'I told Sister Rogers that young men like that should not treat their elders as if they were little children. They will be old themselves one day. Then they will know what it is like to be scolded as if you were in infant school. All I hope is that I will be out of here in time for the coronation. Somebody was telling me the other day that you will be having some of the congregation to see it on the television you are going to have. I'll look forward to that. I remember the coronation of King Edward the Seventh. Mind, they didn't make the fuss of it that they are doing for this one. I expect it's because she is so young, poor soul. Have you seen that big crown she's going to have on her head. It's a wonder it won't break her neck. I don't know how she's going to wear that for such a long time. Let's hope the Archbishop of Canterbury gets a move on, not like that Pentecostal who took a service in the ward last Sunday. I thought he was never going to finish. Half the old girls were snoring long before he came to an end. That's the only good thing I could say about the Reverend Wentworth-Baxter – the service was over before you could say Jack Robinson. How is he doing out in the country, Vicar? I expect he misses Pontywen.'

'He certainly does, Mrs Davies,' I replied. 'Still, he has a lot to keep him occupied with his large family.'

'I should say so,' she said. 'They've got four, haven't they? It's about time they put a stop to things now, I should say. I don't know how that poor little woman can cope with everything, stuck away in the back of beyond like that.'

'I think I had better go, Mrs Davies,' I whispered. 'It looks as if your specialist is coming to see you.'

'You don't have to leave. You can wait outside until he has finished,' she ordered.

'I am afraid not. I have some more people to see.' It was a white lie. I did have other people to see but they were not in the hospital.

As I passed the time of the day with Mr Michael I could see his furrowed brow as he contemplated another encounter with Edwina. 'Nice afternoon,' I said. My greeting received a grunt as a reply.

I strode down the hill from the hospital, which was perched on the hillside outside the town, its red brick standing out against the sparse grass which had survived the fumes of the Valley industry. The sun was shining and I had been rescued from at least another half hour's thraldom with Edwina. My euphoria evaporated as the Rural Dean's bullnosed Morris drew up beside me, on its way downhill from the hospital car park.

'Ah! Vicar!' he bellowed through the open window of his ancient vehicle. 'The very man I want to see!' My heart sank. 'Can you come in beside me for a few moments?' I went in beside him, expecting the worst. Every time I had been in contact with the Reverend Daniel Thomas it meant trouble ahead. 'Well, how are you and how is Dr Sembone?' He was incapable of pronouncing my surname correctly.

'We are both quite well, thank you,' I replied, 'and what can I do for you?' I am afraid I have always led with my chin exposed. My mother used to tell me that my grandfather made the same mistake, which was why he ended up as a docker, and not a headmaster, as he was intended to be, when a promising school teacher.

'Well, Vicar, it's like this,' he intoned through his nose.

'As you know, you are easily the youngest incumbent in our deanery and you have plenty of new ideas and so on. Last Monday the Bishop called a meeting of rural deans and he wants us to move with the times, as he put it. One of the things he wants us to do is to get all our people together for a talk, illustrated with slides which the diocese will provide, and it is about – er – our bodies and how – er –' he paused for a moment, 'babies are – er – conceived, and so on. Now, as far as I can see, you are the only one who can do it, or perhaps Doctor Seaforth wouldn't mind coming along. After all, that's her job, isn't it, and she is a Christian. So if I leave it with you, whether you would mind taking this on or whether you would prefer to ask your good lady, the doctor, to do it, would that be all right?'

The sun was shining through the windscreen. He had wound up his window before I had entered the car. As a result the stale smell of humanity was overpowering, especially when heightened by a strong aroma of moth-balls. I felt an urgent desire to escape. It had been a claustrophobic afternoon. 'By all means, Mr Rural Dean,' I said. 'I shall have a word with my wife this evening and let you know later which of us will do the talk.'

'Splendid,' he replied. 'I would think it would be a good idea if we all came down to your church hall for it. After all, it is bigger than anything else we have in the deanery. Give my kind regards to Dr Seebolm.'

When I told Eleanor of the projected talk, illustrated with slides, she was highly amused. 'A talk about bodies,' she said. 'I would have thought it better to get Matthews the undertaker to do it, with interludes from Full Back Jones on "bodies and how I have buried them". Can you imagine the audience we shall have – an average age of sixty? If they do not know by now about their bodies and what to do with them, nothing I can tell them will be of any use.'

'Don't elaborate any further, my sweet,' I replied.

'Thank you very much. I was not exactly thrilled at the idea.'

I went on to tell her how Edwina had invited herself to our coronation extravaganza at the Vicarage. 'Let's hope that she will still be in hospital then.'

'Don't you believe it,' said Eleanor. 'Should she be in hospital she will have her bed transported here on the back of a lorry if needs be. Once she is determined to do something, nothing will prevent it, come hell or high water. You had better resign yourself to the pleasure of her company on Coronation Day, even if the Queen does not get a word in edgeways. I promise you, Frederick, that she will be in the front row of the audience, giving a running commentary.'

'I think I had better phone the Rural Dean and let him know that you will be giving the birds and the bees lesson,' I said.

'Don't give him the impression that I am eager to oblige,' replied my wife, 'otherwise he will be telling his cronies in the deanery that I am available for Mothers' Union talks on woman's problems at the drop of a hat. Make it appear that I am doing this as a great favour in the middle of an extremely busy schedule. It's a one-off effort, tell him.'

It took some time before he answered the phone. 'Have you been ringing long?' he said. 'We were listening to a programme on the wireless about Westminster Abbey – very interesting.'

'Don't you let me keep you, Mr Rural Dean. I am just letting you know that my wife is willing to give the talk about our bodies. She is a very busy lady but she will try to fit it in to her schedule of work. Perhaps you will let me know a date as soon as possible. In the meanwhile, I think I had better let you get back to your programme.'

'Oh, thank you very much, Vicar. Tell Dr Seymour that we are delighted she can do it. Talking about Westminster Abbey . . .' my heart sank for the second time that day, 'I was at the bank with Mr Vaughan-Jenkins after I left you. He tells me that you are going to have a television set from your brother so that you can watch the coronation. Isn't that kind of him? I am afraid that we are not going to be so lucky. I wonder if you wouldn't mind Mrs Thomas and myself joining some of your congregation at the Vicarage to see the service. We haven't anybody in the parish who has a television set. You know what these old farmers are like. They won't part with their pennies, will they?'

I took a deep breath. 'Come along by all means, Mr Rural Dean. I am afraid you will have to put up with some very cramped seating arrangements because so many people want to come. Let me know the suggested date for the talk as soon as possible, would you please?'

'Well, thank you very much for inviting us to see the coronation at your Vicarage. That is very kind of you, indeed. Mrs Thomas will be delighted. Thank you very much indeed.' With that he put the phone down.

I came into the sitting room where Eleanor was listening to Beethoven's Seventh Symphony on the Third Programme. 'You should have been listening to a talk on Westminster Abbey on the other wavelength,' I said. 'It has so intrigued the Rural Dean that he has invited himself and his wife to view the coronation in this Vicarage, together with half of the population of Pontywen.'

'Do you know what?' said my wife. 'I think our viewers will provide much more amusement than any coronation service. What a wonderful mixture, the Rural Dean, Edwina Davies, Charlie Hughes manipulating his hearing aid, our son and daughter who must be there to witness the historic occasion, not to mention Bertie Owen who is bound to gatecrash the party. I can't wait for 2 June. Incidentally did he give any indication of when he wants this "moving with the times" educational project?'

'My dear love,' I replied, 'once he knew that he had a reserved seat for the great day, he had forgotten about the Bishop's pioneering adventure into the sociological and biological realms. All that mattered was that he and his good lady would be in Pontywen Vicarage on 2 June. I hope we don't get any more self-invited people for the occasion.'

'I can only think of one other invasion,' said Eleanor.

'And who is that?' I asked.

'Charles and Bronwen plus their four, just to make up the number.'

'Don't tempt fate, there's a dear,' I said.

'Stranger things than that have happened,' she replied.

Next morning the curate appeared at Matins with a smile on his face. 'You are looking happy, Emlyn. I take it that you have slain the dragon.'

He answered my comment with a chuckle. 'Something like that. I'll tell you all after the service.' Considering that it was the last day before Holy Week, there was a noticeable lack of solemnity in our devotions. He looked as if a load had been lifted from his shoulders and I was glad for his sake. He was too good natured to be persecuted by a frustrated fifty-year-old headmistress. Emlyn stayed on his knees for quite a while after Matins was over, evidently giving thanks for his deliverance.

'Coming in for coffee?' I asked when he joined me eventually.

'Yes, please, Vicar, and you can have a blow by blow account of the *coup de grâce* which laid low the dragon, as you put it, yesterday evening, thanks to Dr Secombe's advice.'

We were joined in the sitting room by Eleanor, who was anxious to here what had transpired. 'Well, Dr Secombe . . .' he began.

'I think it's about time you started calling me Eleanor,' she said, 'but carry on, do.'

'Well, Eleanor, you advised me that a face-to-face confrontation with Miss Harding was the only way I could end this constant chasing after me, so I invited her to come to my place last night. I must admit that I filled myself with Dutch courage before she arrived. It was the only way I was going to say my piece. When I opened the door to her knock, there she was in her best clothes, a special hair do and enough perfume to drown the whisky on my breath and that was a lot, believe me. Evidently she thought her big moment had come. "Sit down, Miss Harding," I said in my best scout-master voice once we were in the front room. "Virginia, please." She tried to sound like a sex kitten. It was grotesque – so grotesque I felt sorry for her. "Now then, Miss Harding," I went on, "I think the time has come to put all the cards on the table. You have been ringing me up incessantly, even at two o'clock in the morning. I have had enough. I want nothing to do with you, Miss Harding. I have my own life to live and I am asking you to keep out of it. You have your own life to live and I would have thought that your career would have a lot of satisfaction in it. That's all I want to say, Miss Harding. I am sorry to have to be so blunt but you give me no choice." I had learnt that speech by heart. I rehearsed it over and over again until I could say it in my sleep. You can have no idea of how she looked when I had finished. I had a dog once. I spoilt it but one day it made a mess all over the place. I belted it right, left and centre. It looked at me just as she did. She got up and went out of the house. She didn't say a single word and that was it. I hated doing it but it was the only way, wasn't it?' He looked for reassurance from us both.

'My dear Emlyn,' said my wife, 'there was no alternative. You had to be cruel to be kind. She will get over it in the fullness of time. Everything heals after the surgeon's knife has been applied.'

That afternoon we had a family outing into the surrounding countryside to pick bunches of pussy willow for the Palm Sunday service the following morning. It was the custom for the children to bring 'English palm', the old name for the willow buds, in procession to the altar while the hymn 'All glory, laud and honour' was sung. I had never forgotten how when I first came to Pontywen the children from the council estate who were unable to escape by car into the countryside had to beg a few scrawny twiglets from the privileged few whose parents had cars. I remember particularly one incident when a spoiled child arrived outside the church with his arms full of pussy willow. I asked him to share some of his abundance with two little boys alongside him. He searched amongst the profusion until he found two little pieces with a few buds on them. He presented one each to his classmates with an air of generosity which was more appropriate to a golden handshake than the mean spirited response to my request. After that I organised a search for bundles of 'English palm' every Saturday before Palm Sunday and each child had an ample supply to hold in procession. This year David was going to join the parade for the first time and he was more excited about that than he was at the thought of the Easter egg a week later. Baby Elspeth would have to be content with receiving a palm cross when her mother brought her to the altar rails. Unlike David when he was an infant in arms, she had been a model of good behaviour at morning service, receiving the equivalent of four gold stars from the elderly ladies in the congregation for her behaviour.

The weather was warm and sunny. We decided to drive to Abergavenny to collect our Palm Sunday bunches on the way and then to spend on hour or so in the pleasant little market town to do a little shopping and to have tea in one of its cafés. We stopped at a river bank on the way and Eleanor joined me in a very productive haul of willow buds, while David watched from inside the car, alongside his sleeping sister. We loaded the greenery into the boot, after presenting my son with a twig or two to keep him quiet.

'Are these mine for tomorrow?' he asked.

'If you are a good boy you can have a lot more tomorrow,' I said.

'Can't Elspeth have some, Dad?'

'She's too small to be in the procession. She can't walk yet, can she?'

'Can't mummy carry her?'

'No, David, the procession is only for children who can walk. Mummy will bring her up to the altar to have a palm cross.'

'Can I have a palm cross as well?'

'Of course you can. Don't you remember coming up for one last year? The one you've got pinned on the wall above your bed? Elspeth wasn't born then. So she can have one on the wall over her cot this year.'

When we pulled into the car park in Abergavenny Eleanor said, 'Don't look now, keep your head down, there's a dear.'

'Don't look at what?' I asked.

'It's a family group just disappearing in the distance. Bronwen carrying one on her arm and the other hand holding another as the child tried to walk. Charles inevitably walking ahead with the two eldest on either hand, like a Middle Eastern husband accustomed to having his wife bringing up the rear. So let's stay here for a few minutes and let them get away. I'm afraid, if we meet them I shall have to explode and spoil a lovely afternoon.'

'After what you said last night about Charles and Bronwen joining our coronation audience I think we should abandon our shopping expedition in Abergavenny and have it in Pontywen instead.'

'Having come all this way, Frederick, I don't feel inclined to turn back simply because we have seen Mr and Mrs Wentworth-Baxter and family. Why should they spoil our afternoon out? Another couple of minutes and they will have gone out of sight. All we have to do is to avoid the market. Charles is sure to be in there after a bargain. They won't be in a café. He won't want to fork out for a meal there. So avoid the market and avoid the main street but, first of all, let's find a café and have something to eat. I'm starving.'

'Righto. Upon your head be it. There's a café down that street by the market.'

We waited another five minutes to be sure that we were in the clear and then made our way out of the car park. Eleanor was pushing Elspeth in the pushchair and I had a firm hold on David's hand, which was tugging me like an unruly colt resenting its constraint. When we reached the café we found it full. If we wished to wait for a table, we could do so, we were told. We had no wish to wait for a table and came out to look for somewhere else to eat. The streets were full of half the farming population around Abergavenny, not to mention the day trippers who had come up from the valleys.

'For heaven's sake,' exclaimed Eleanor, 'let's put our hands in our pockets and go to the hotel across the road. Whatever we have to pay, it will be worth it, just to avoid all this shoving and pushing. I know one thing. We shan't find Charles and his family there; that's for certain.'

We crossed the street and passed through the portals of the three-star hotel. Once inside we found a haven of peace. It was a Georgian building where time had stood still. There was a young lady whose white blouse and black tie surmounted the reception desk.

'Can I help you?' she inquired in an accent she had

evidently acquired only recently since her rural origins were barely concealed.

'Do you serve afternoon teas?' said Eleanor.

'Not until four o'clock, madam. You can wait in the lounge until then, if you like.' It was half past three. We decided to wait. Elspeth was fast asleep in the push chair and David's eyelids were beginning to droop. There was no one in the lounge. Copies of the *Daily Telegraph* and *The Times* were on the highly polished table in the centre of the room. Soon David was asleep beside us on the big settee by the window. I was attempting to solve *The Times* crossword without using a pencil and my wife was reading the Saturday features page in the *Telegraph*. Suddenly the peace of our oasis was shattered by an all too familiar voice telling Simon to be quiet. We both dropped our newspapers and looked at each other in dismay. The very person we had planned to avoid was about to descend on us. Four-year-old Simon led the invasion, followed by his father shouting at him to stop running. Charles Wentworth-Baxter caught sight of us on the settee and stood transfixed. His dismay seemed to be much greater than ours. To use one of Idris the Milk's favourite expressions, he was trapped 'like a fly in a jam jar'.

Charles was rescued from his predicament by Bronwen's appearance from behind him. She was coping with three children but found enough breath to exclaim, 'Look, Charles! Fred and Eleanor.' He was still speechless. However, Eleanor was not.

'How nice to see you, Bronwen.' She stood up and moved towards her, ignoring her husband. 'Let me take the baby from you for a moment,' she added. 'It looks as if you could do with some assistance.'

By now Charles had ceased to be a statue and had grabbed Simon by his coat collar. 'Now, behave yourself,' he warned him, 'or I'll have to smack you.'

'Hello, Simon,' I said. 'You are going to be a good boy, aren't you?' He nodded his head. 'When are you going to start school?'

'In September, tell the Vicar,' said Bronwen. 'Fancy meeting you here. We are celebrating Charles's birthday. So we thought we would come somewhere decent for our tea.'

She was a changed person since my last encounter with her. Her self-confidence had returned and she looked well groomed, unlike the slattern of not so long ago. I managed to squeeze out a half-hearted 'Happy birthday, Charles.' My wife stayed silent.

Ten minutes later when we went into the restaurant for tea, Eleanor and Bronwen were in animated conversation and I was left with a sullen ex-curate whose birthday was apparently far from happy. Our two families occupied adjoining tables. David was now wide awake and was very interested in Simon who was not very interested in David. Every overture from my son to the eldest Wentworth-Baxter child was rejected out of hand, despite the encouragement from Bronwen to get her offspring to talk to David. He was as reticent as his father, who spoke no more than a few sentences all through tea. It was a most uncomfortable experience. I was very glad when the time came to settle the bills.

'See you soon,' said Eleanor to Bronwen when we went our different ways. Charles glared at her. The glare was returned. As we sauntered up the main street, with my wife manoeuvring the push chair past a multitude of legs, I said to her. 'What a pain in the neck that was!'

'For you, maybe,' she replied, 'but I was delighted to see the transformation in Bronwen. Her father must have frightened the life out of Charles. From what she said to me in the "Ladies", he now helps out in the house, even if it is a grudging assistance. He knows that if he falls out of line again that will mean curtains for him.'

'Falls out of line!' I exclaimed. 'From my past experience with Charles, I would say that is inevitable.'

'Well,' said Eleanor, 'that will be his funeral, not hers. Her parents are more than willing to look after her, should it come to the worst. In the meanwhile we must give her all the support we can. That's why I have invited her over to join our throng of coronation viewers, together with the children. If he wants to come, I suppose he can. I told you I had a hunch about it. Anyway, I said she could include him in the invite. What else was I to do?'

I was about to suggest an alternative and then decided against it, in case I was accused of a lack of Christian charity. 'As you please,' I replied, 'but it sounds like a manufactured hunch to me.'

10

The next morning, a sunny beginning to Palm Sunday, the children from the two Sunday Schools were forming a noisy scrum outside the parish church. Some had come with their own bunches of 'pussy willow'. Included amongst them was my young son, standing on the fringe, hopping excitedly from foot to foot. The others were waiting impatiently to be supplied with their share of the barrow load being wheeled up the path by Bertie Owen in his capacity as Superintendent of St Padarn's Sunday School. 'Bertie!' shouted Idris the Milk, who had been trying to keep order unsuccessfully. 'You are dropping more branches than you've got on the barrow.' Whereupon there was a rush from several of the branchless to retrieve pieces for themselves.

'Quiet!' I bellowed. 'Now get into line.'

Emlyn Howells and I had just followed the choir on their way from the vestry door to the front of the church, ready to lead the procession of palm bearers. When all the children had been provided with bunches I moved into the church to announce the hymn 'All glory, laud and honour'. As the organ blasted the opening notes, with all the stops pulled out by Mr Greenfield, the cross bearer came to the fore, prepared for action. Harry Llewellyn, a tall, pimply youth, lowered the processional cross to get it through the door as if it were a lance. He struck Bertie Owen between the shoulder blades as he was about to make his way down the aisle to collect the 'pussy willow' in the sanctuary. The Sunday School superintendent was propelled into a collision with a pile of hymn books and ended up lying spreadeagled at my feet, face down and covered with *Hymns Ancient and Modern*. In the meanwhile the congregation had launched into a lusty rendering of the first verse. I bent down to help Bertie to his feet but he was back to a standing position before I could render assistance. He had been an athlete in his time and was a very fit man. If his mental ability had matched his physical attributes, he would have been a force to be reckoned with. As it was, all his strength was in his body. To quote Idris, he had 'a vacuum upstairs'.

'You be careful with that thing, Harry,' he said. 'Next time it could be an old lady and a hospital job.'

It took another verse before the procession could get

moving. During the hold up, some of the children had begun to have 'pussy willow' contests to while away the time. As my curate said afterwards, it was not a procession but a shambling amble when it reached the altar rails – young David arrived at the end of the line and refused to surrender his 'English palm' to Bertie. Instead he invaded the sanctuary to present it to me, much to the delight of the old ladies in the congregation who told me after the service that they thought it was 'lovely'. Having made his presentation, he proceeded to dash down the chancel and then fall flat on his face. Like Bertie, he was up on his feet quickly and proudly joined his mother and his sister in the front pew.

I began my pulpit address by questioning the children about the events of Palm Sunday. 'How did Jesus come into Jerusalem on Palm Sunday?' I asked. A host of hands went up. I picked on Shirley Evans, the nine-year-old daughter of one of the sidesmen.

'He was riding on a donkey.'

'Why do you think he did that?' There was a pause before Selwyn Owen raised his hand. He was a twelve-year-old who fancied himself as a wag in my confirmation class.

'Because he couldn't find a horse.' There was an outburst of laughter from the children and a few from the adults. It was confrontation time.

'Selwyn,' I said, 'do you realise that we are entering the most sacred week of the year and all you can do is try to be funny about someone who gave his life for you on Good Friday? He chose to ride on a donkey because in the Old Testament the prophet Zechariah told the Jews that when the Messiah came to Jerusalem he would be riding on a donkey. In those days, the donkey was regarded as a noble animal. Nowadays a donkey is a term applied to someone foolish and empty headed. I need say no more.'

The silence that followed my remark was sufficient to ensure that the rest of my address made its full impact. The distribution of palm crosses at the conclusion of the service was followed sometimes by sword fights with them in the pews. Today there were none. Selwyn Owen had been the catalyst for a most effective Palm Sunday service.

As I was shaking hands with the congregation as they left, Idris the Milk come up behind me and whispered in my ear that he would like to speak to me later. When the last worshipper had left me, he joined me. 'I don't know whether you have heard, Vicar, but it seems that the Council are arranging a big fireworks display at the Welfare Ground on the night of the coronation. It won't be anything like that fiasco after VS day, when Bertie Owen set off all the fireworks at once in the square and we all had to dive for cover when that rocket went through Protheroe's plate-glass window. This is going to be well run with show pieces and all that jazz. What about our big concert that night? Everybody will want to go to the Welfare Ground.'

'No, I hadn't heard about that, Idris,' I replied.

'We had better call an emergency meeting of the Committee as soon as possible.'

'Can you let everybody know by Wednesday?'

'Easily, Vicar. Perhaps we can have an eve of the coronation "do", but let's see what the others have got to say.'

By the time we met on the Wednesday evening, full details of the Council's programme of celebrations had been published in the local newspaper. All the schools would be giving coronation mugs. The Pontywen Silver Band was booked to play on the Welfare Ground in the afternoon. The Mayor would be visiting all the street parties and attending the fireworks spectacular later in the evening. A grand dance was to take place at Abergelly Miners' Welfare Hall, admission free.

'Well, Mr Chairman,' said David Vaughan-Jenkins, 'I think our programme compares with that. We have a slap-up tea arranged for our children and, by the way, I think the Mayor should visit that. We have pony rides and boxes of coronation chocolates for the children. We have a dance, too, to finish up the evening, admission free, and in Pontywen, not Abergelly. Our big headache is what to do about our splendid concert. Everybody will want to go to the fireworks, that's positive. If we hold it later in the week that will be an anticlimax. All the excitement will have gone by then, I am afraid.'

'If I may make a suggestion, Mr Chairman, why not have our big concert on the eve of the coronation,' Idris suggested. 'As you know, I had a word with you about this after church on Sunday. Since then I have been in touch with Aneurin Williams who is going to be responsible for putting it on and he says that he is quite prepared to have the show the night before. It will be one up for us as a church to be the first to get the festivities going in Pontywen.'

This suggestion brought Mrs Agnes Collier to her feet. She had been made responsible for the catering. 'Now hold on,' she warned. 'What is going to happen to all the arrangements we have made to get the hall ready for the tea the night before? If you are going to have this big concert, there will be all the chairs and tables to get ready. You can't expect the women to be working late into the night. We'll all be wanting to listen to the service or watch it, if we are one of the lucky ones, the next morning. So I don't see how you are going to be able to have your concert. It's one thing to say that Aneurin Williams is prepared to do it. He doesn't have to clear away and get everything ready.'

There was a lull in the proceedings as the Committee members sought to find ideas which would overcome the obstacle raised by the catering supremo.

'What about a working party, ready to begin the clearing away, etc. as soon as the concert was over! There are plenty of men who would be willing to lend a hand.' This contribution came from Harold Jones, builder and Vicar's warden. 'Perhaps we could start the concert earlier so that there would be that much more time to get on with things.'

'I don't know about starting the concert earlier,' said Idris. 'Some of the men won't finish work until five o'clock at the earliest and then they've got to have their meal and clean up before they leave the house.'

'Come off it,' retorted Harold. 'Most of the men are on shift work. That means that those working six till two will be OK. Anybody doing the two till ten would not be able to take part anyway, except by taking French leave. You are just talking about the white-collar workers and there aren't many of them. I still think that starting the concert at half past six could solve the problem. What do you think, Agnes?'

'I suppose that would be all right, as long as there's this working party of men to get cracking straight away after the concert,' she said somewhat reluctantly. 'Mind, the women will still have to get the cloths on the table and see to the crockery and so on. It's going to be a late night for everybody, I can see, but let me tell you now if there's no working party when we want them, don't ever ask the women to do anything like this again.' I put Harold Jones's proposition to the meeting, and they voted unanimously in favour.

'Now, then, Vicar,' Agnes was on her feet once again, 'what about these lists you are going to put up in the porch for people to sign if they want to come and watch the television? I think you said, only two from one family can come. It's fine for me because I am a widow, as you know, but it's a bit hard on some of the families.'

'Look, Mrs Collier,' I said heatedly, 'I have said it before and must say it again: nobody has a right to enter someone else's house to watch the ceremony. It's only through the kindness of television set owners that they are invited. I can tell you now that already we have a number of people coming to the Vicarage to see the programme and I know that Mr Vaughan-Jenkins and Mr Nicholls are similarly placed. I shall put up a list in St Mary's and St Padarn's on Easter Day. There is no guarantee that there will be room for them. The only thing that will be fair is to put all the names into a hat and call out the lucky numbers. If I had a set the size of a cinema screen and put it in the hall it still would not be enough to cope with all those who would want to come. To be quite frank, I am beginning to wish I had not been given a set, if it is going to cause any animosity. I would have been quite content to listen to the service on the wireless as I did in 1937 at the last coronation.' Very rarely did I lose my temper at meetings of any kind but the self-invitations of the Rural Dean and Edwina Davies plus Eleanor's open-house invite to Bronwen, Charles and family had exacerbated the soreness of a raw nerve. To have Agnes Collier adding to the discomfort was too much to bear.

The sight of the Vicar losing his temper was sufficient to end any further discussion of the television issue. It was decided to hold the next meeting in a fortnight's time.

'I can appreciate how you feel,' said David Vaughan-Jenkins as we left the church hall. 'It is amazing how friendly people become when they know you will be watching the big day on your own set. I expect by the time the next coronation comes, everybody will have their own.'

'I wish that time had arrived in 1952,' I replied. 'It would have saved me a lot of worry. How on earth are we going to cope with the Rural Dean and his wife, Edwina Davies, the Wentworth-Baxters and a crowd from the congregation, I do not know.'

'I'll tell you one thing, Vicar, between you and me and the gatepost, your wife will be much more of a help that day than mine.' With that remark from the churchwarden we went our different ways, leaving me to regret my fit of sulks at Eleanor's invitation to Bronwen.

The following day was the date for my visit to Father Joe McNally's residence to finalise details of the renting of St Padarn's for a late-morning Sunday morning Mass. He rang me during the morning to remind me to bring a music copy of *Hymns Ancient and Modern* with me. 'What with your tenor and my bass we should be able to do it justice, that we should.'

Before I left, Eleanor warned me to be careful about the quantity of alcohol I might be tempted to drink. 'Remember Bill Jackson,' she said. He was Vicar of a neighbouring parish who had been arrested for being drunk in charge of his Austin Seven. His parishioners said that he always drove as if he was drunk in charge, not knowing his right hand from his left hand and since he drove so slowly his miniature car would be in greater danger of damage than any pedestrian with whom it might collide. 'Remember you have a bigger car and drive much faster than that unfortunate gentleman,' she added. With these words ringing in my ears I proceeded up the drive circumspectly to impress my spouse. Once outside the gates I reverted to my normal speed, as undoubtedly she guessed I would.

'St Francis of Assisi' was a small red brick church on the outskirts of Abergelly and alongside it was the presbytery, which was almost as big as the place of worship. The drive gates were open, ready to accommodate my car. As soon as I pulled up, Father Joe came from the house.

'Irish territory in splendid isolation,' he said as he put his arm around my shoulders and escorted me into the lounge. There by the window, was an upright piano, bearing the name 'Challen', its polished exterior paying tribute to the handiwork of his housekeeper.

'I see you have brought your means of singing for your supper,' he said, opening the lid of the piano and taking the hymn book from me. He placed it on the music stand

and drew the music stool to the piano. Then he paused. 'But before we raise the roof we must anoint our throats with some Irish embrocation,' he ordered. He went to a side table on which was a full bottle of whiskey. 'Now, by the time you leave tonight, that bottle has to be emptied,' he ordered. He poured out half a tumblerful each for us. 'Here's to a long and enjoyable friendship.' We touched glasses and he sat down at the piano. 'What shall we have as our introit?' he asked.

'To get us off to a rousing start,' I suggested, 'I would say Hymn Number 196. People have told me that they can hear this being sung at Cardiff Arms Park half a mile away, known to every rugby supporter as 'Guidemeo'.

'Good old Cwm Rhondda,' he replied. 'Do you know the story of the millionaire who used to sing in the second verse "land my safe on Jordan's side", instead of "land me safe on Jordan's side"? Somebody should have told him that he couldn't take it with him.' He turned the pages till he found 196 and then played through the tune with the touch of a skilled pianist. 'Are you ready, Freddy?' he asked.

For the next half hour or so, we sang all the old favourites. He had a deep rich voice and sang almost as well as he played. Then there was a knock on the door after we had finished 'The day thou gavest, Lord, has ended'.

'Dinner's ready, Father,' announced a female Irish voice.

'It certainly has not ended,' he said. 'We must carry on with our hymns of praise once our stomachs are full, after a decent rest, of course.'

We went into the dining room. My heart sank when I

saw two bottles of wine on the table, one white, one red. 'Joe!' I gasped, 'how do you expect me to drive back to Pontywen after imbibing all that lot? My wife has already warned me not to drink to excess.'

'Now then, Fred, don't panic, there's a good lad. We are going to fill our stomachs with three courses of excellent food. That will absorb a lot of alcohol. If you can't finish the whiskey afterwards, I'll do it for you. I shall see that you are in a fit state to drive back, even if it means making you walk a straight line down the path before you get into your car.'

If he was not right about the absorption of alcohol he was certainly right about the excellent food. We began with a creamed vegetable soup, followed by a delicious steak and kidney pie and attendant vegetables and crowned by a sherry trifle with apricots and almonds and a liberal application from the bottle of sherry. This was rounded off with Stilton cheese and biscuits, accompanied by a glass of port. It was one of the best meals I had ever eaten and the cook was a little old Irish lady with a thick accent which seemed to indicate that she had spent most of her life in some remote village in south-west Ireland. When she came to collect our plates, prior to our moving back into the lounge, I said to her, 'I must thank you for a wonderful meal. I can recommend your cooking to anybody who wants to know what good food tastes like.' She blushed, murmured her appreciation and made a bee-line for the door.

Back in the lounge, I said to Joe, 'Where did she learn to cook like that? You have a treasure in that housekeeper of yours.'

'You needn't tell me that,' he replied. 'As it happens,

she is an aunt of mine, several times removed. She came to London many years ago to find work, like so many others. Eventually she became cook housekeeper to a moneyed family in Kensington. She stayed with them until the husband left his wife, just before the war. After that she kept house for a priest in Chelsea. He died suddenly five years ago. I was moving into this, my first parish, and I needed a housekeeper and that's it.'

'You're a lucky man, Joe,' I said.

'Now, come off it, Fred,' he replied, 'the boot is on the other foot. You have a charming and very capable wife and you have two children. Would you care to swap with me?'

'Touché,' I murmured. Then I went on, 'May I ask you a question? There must be times when you feel very lonely. When you came to welcome me, you mentioned the words "splendid isolation". You are obviously a man who enjoys life, very much an extrovert, if I may say so. With a personality like yours, surely you must miss the companionship of a woman and the love of a family. You would be an excellent family man. If the time ever came when the Pope decreed that married clergy would be allowed within the priesthood, would you settle down with a wife?'

'That,' he said with a certain amount of vehemence, 'is a question I will not answer. Shall we get down to working out the details of our lease-lend agreement, to use a wartime phrase?' I could see that I had done an 'Agnes Collier' and touched a raw nerve. I determined that I would never again question the celibacy of the priesthood in our conversations.

We agreed that he should have the use of the altar

from 11.30 a.m. until 12.30 p.m., every Sunday for the next three months for a rental of ten pounds a Sunday. Since the rental provided an income almost equal to our normal Sunday collection at St Padarn's, it was a lucrative transaction. After we had shaken hands on the deal we sang some more hymns 'Ancient and Modern' concluded with 'Now thank we all our God'. There was still a half bottle of whiskey.

'If you don't mind,' I said, 'in the interests of road safety and the condition of my liver, may I suggest that you have a very large nightcap while I remove my vehicle from your drive and go back to Pontywen while I still know the way.'

'It is a wise man who knows his own limits,' he replied. He came to see me off the premises, ignoring the heavy rain which was falling. When I had reversed on to the road, he said, 'If you drive forwards as well as you drive backwards, you'll have no trouble in getting home at all. May God and St Christopher go with you; see you at St Padarn's one of these days.' With that, he patted the bonnet of the car and waved me away.

I drove off in a euphoric haze. 'Brimful of the friendliness that in an RC presbytery I have found,' I said to myself, quoting a revised line from one of Keats's sonnets. Fortified by Joe's prayer that God and St Christopher should protect me, I was relishing the prospect of an open road with not a car in sight. Suddenly it happened. A rabbit darted out from a hedge and froze into immobility in the glare of my headlights. On my one and only excursion into the realm of field sports, I had maimed a rabbit with my one and only attempt at marksmanship. I had the repugnant obligation to club it to death with the shotgun. After that, I vowed I would never kill another rabbit.

I slammed my foot on the brake and swerved at the same time to avoid the creature. The car skidded on the wet road. It ended up on its roof with the wheels spinning and with my head in a similar condition. In a daze I reached out for the ignition key and turned off the engine. My right shoulder and my ribs felt as if they had been hit by a two-ton truck. I lay on my back, still for a minute or so. Then I decided to clamber out. Since the driving seat was only inches away from the hedge there was no alternative but to make my escape through the other door. As I strove to move towards it, lifting my leg over the gear lever, my whole body was racked with pain. 'I am here for the night,' I thought.

It was then that in the distance the headlights of a car appeared. I prayed that God and St Christopher had sent them. Sure enough, as the vehicle approached, it slowed down and stopped. Four men got out. In no time at all, they turned the car over on to its four wheels. Next, one of them squeezed himself between the hedge and the door of the driving seat. He opened it and inquired, 'Are you hurt, Reverend?'

'I don't think so,' I replied hesitantly.

'Can you manage to get out this side?' he asked. I raised myself from the seat painfully and took his hand. Between us I managed to edge myself out on the grass verge.

'My shoulder and my ribs are aching but, apart from that, I feel all right,' I said.

'Sure now?' he inquired again.

'Yes, sure,' I replied.

The other three came to join him. 'I tell you what,

Reverend,' one of them said, his speech slurred by alcohol, 'we thought you'd 'ad it when we saw the car first, didn't we, Mal?'

Mal was evidently the driver since his friends seemed incapable. 'All right, boys, you get back in,' he ordered. After they had seated themselves he said, 'Let's watch you go on your way first, Reverend. Just to see that you're all right.' Then lowering his voice, he added, 'It's been my turn to drive tonight. We go out once a week for a booze up but one of us is always the unlucky one to be on orange juice. Still, you can't risk life and limb when you're driving, can you?'

When I arrived at the Vicarage, Eleanor was still up. 'Good heavens!' she exclaimed, 'What has happened to you, love? You look as pale as a ghost.'

I recounted the story of my misadventure.

'Come on, take your shirt off. Let's examine you,' she ordered. After a brief examination, she pronounced the verdict. 'No bones broken, but you'll have some lovely bruises in the morning.'

'It's a good thing that God and St Christopher were protecting me,' I said.

She replied, 'Since you smell like a brewery, you can thank them that you did not end up in a police station. Let that be a lesson to you, my lad.' I was never allowed to forget that lesson thereafter.

11

'All I can say about these slides and the accompanying notes is that they would be far more suitable for infant schools.' Eleanor's comment came after a brief perusal of the so-called 'information pack' to be used in the moral welfare project for sex education in the rural deanery. I had ignored her suggestion that the Rural Dean should 'keep his slides', as she put it.

Now they had arrived at the Vicarage on the Tuesday morning, ready for showing to our rural deanery in Pontywen church hall on the following Friday evening. 'To expect me, as a doctor, to lecture adults, most of whom are long past their teens, in the meaning of sex in such terms is an insult to my vocation and training. As for those who are to be lectured, it treats them as if they still believed that babies were delivered by storks and found behind gooseberry bushes. I shall borrow some illustrated material from the sister tutor at the hospital and give the lecture in my own way. If some of them find it shocking, so be it. Most of the teenage pregnancies nowadays stem from the lack of guidance from parents, who either think it is not quite nice to talk about sexual relations or who pretend that "the kids will find out for themselves soon enough, the same as we did". It is not good enough, Fred. It really isn't.' Her face was flushed with anger.

'I shall look forward to next Friday evening,' I replied.

'I shall spend most of my time looking at the old ladies' faces and a fair amount watching the Rural Dean's reaction. It will have the same effect as if they had been taken to see an X film in Cardiff, with disbelief and horror at what is being unfolded before their very eyes.'

'Not so much before their eyes, dope,' she said, 'as what is assaulting their ears. Almost all of my lecture will be with no illustrations. What a pity Charles is no longer in the deanery. He would have learned a lot about the right way to treat a woman.'

Any further discussion was prevented by a ring on the door bell. It was Heather Andrews with Christine, her baby daughter. 'I've taken advantage of this lovely sunny morning to walk down from Ashburnham Close to get some exercise. If I am to be running alongside my pony, giving children rides in a few week' time, I shall have to be fit, believe me,' she said.

'Coming down was easy,' replied my wife. 'You wait until you push that big pram back up the hill. Now that really will be exercise. So I suggest a cup of coffee and some biscuits to build you up for the return journey.'

'If you don't mind,' I said, 'I shall leave you two ladies alone for your *tête-à-tête* while I get on with some sick visiting.'

'Before you go, Fred, I suppose that everything has been cleared for me to give the rides for the afternoon of D-Day.' Heather sounded concerned. 'I understand that they are planning a big firework display on the Welfare Ground in the evening, which means that there will be plenty of activity going on while I am doing my thing with the children.'

'As far as I know, Idris the Milk, who is the secretary

of our organising committee, has checked with the council that everything is OK. He is very reliable. Anyway I'll pop into his house on my way back from visiting just to make sure.' So saying, I left them in the lounge and went into the study to collect my robes and sick Communion set for my monthly celebrations of Holy Communion in the homes of house-bound parishioners. No sooner had I gone into the study than there was a telephone call.

'Good morning, Vicar.' It was my Bishop.

'Good morning, my lord,' I replied.

'I expect you have heard that Canon Joseph Morris is retiring at Abergelly. As you know, he has been there for nearly forty years and his health is beginning to deteriorate. The parish needs an infusion of young blood in the Vicarage. The living is in my gift and I wondered if you might be interested. As you know, it is a much larger parish than Pontywen and dominates the valley industrially, but not, I am afraid, ecclesiastically. You have now been in Pontywen for eight years and I wondered whether you would like a change. I would suggest that you go to see the parish and its church and to have a word with Canon Morris. If you do not leave Pontywen, after you have been to see Abergelly, I shall understand fully how you feel. However, please pay it a visit and then let me know in your own good time your decision.' The unexpected offer of a new living rendered me speechless for a few moments. Then I recovered my senses.

'Thank you for considering me for this important parish,' I breathed. 'I shall certainly pay it a visit, as you suggest, and then talk things over with my wife who has her practice in Pontywen. It will have to be a joint decision, as you will appreciate, my lord.'

'Of course,' he replied. 'There is no hurry. The Canon is not due to retire until the end of May, in any case.'

I put the phone down and went back to the lounge, where Eleanor and Heather were engaged in a conversation about breast feeding, as far as I could gather.'

'I thought you were on your way out,' said my wife.

'I'm afraid I was delayed by his lordship,' I replied. 'I'll tell you about it when I get back. It involves you as well as me.'

'Tell me now,' she demanded.

'When I come back,' I reiterated.

'You rotten thing,' she shouted as I went out to the car. On my way to Mrs Turvey in Balaclava Street, my mind was in a turmoil. I had assumed that I would be in Pontywen for many years to come as part of a 'working partnership' – myself: the local parson; my wife: the local doctor. This offer had come like a bolt from the blue and threatened our domestic bliss. I began to wish the Bishop had never phoned.

When I arrived at the Turvey residence, the district nurse answered the door. Beryl Evans had been one of the bridesmaids at the Wentworth-Baxter wedding. A contemporary of Bronwen's at Pontywen Hospital, she had been appointed only recently to work in the town. A tall, talkative young lady, she made an ideal visitor for the bed-ridden, ready for a chat at any time and strong enough to lift any invalid who needed a bed change or a bed bath.

'She's ready for you, Vicar,' she announced. 'Is there anything you want for the service? I've put a nice clean cloth on the table by her bed and a little jug of water.'

'That's fine,' I said.

'How is Bronwen these days?' she asked. 'I hear she has four children already. I never thought Charles could be such a fast worker.'

'Oh, she's OK,' I replied. 'Her hands are tied with such a large family, not to mention the fast worker. You must call on her one day. I am sure she will be glad to see you. She needs to see fresh faces, stuck out in the country, as she is.'

'I must do that,' she answered. 'When I get a break from this busy routine.' Then she lowered her voice. 'By the way, Mrs Turvey is going downhill, I'm afraid. The doctor doesn't give her long to live, a few months at the most, but she is very cheerful, all the same.' She led me into the front room, where the old lady was sitting up, propped up by two big pillows. She was a tiny lady whose body was bent in half by rheumatoid arthritis, her hands were clenched permanently by the cruel disease and her legs were locked in an equally permanent bent position. Her white hair had been brushed and combed. Despite the incessant pain and discomfort, her face was always beaming whenever I came to visit her.

'Good morning, Vicar. Isn't it a lovely day.' She made a valiant effort to lift her head to look at me, her little face alight with a smile of greeting.

'It certainly is, Mrs Turvey,' I said, 'and all the better for seeing you.'

'I expect you say that to all the girls,' she replied. She had never lost her sense of humour despite the suffering which afflicted her. Her daughter said it was her secret weapon and that without it she would have been dead years ago.

'Our Ethel is working this morning but Nurse Evans has been very good and has put everything ready.'

As I prepared the Communion vessels and robed for the service, she engaged in a monologue. 'I hear they're going to have fireworks on the Welfare Ground for the coronation. I hope they make a better show of that than they did for VE day in the square. That was the last time I was out of the house. Our Ethel took me there in a wheelchair. I said to her, I don't know why Bertie Owen wasted all these rockets in one go. I could have done with one of them behind my wheelchair. It would have saved you pushing and what's more I would have been home on time. I can remember King George the Fifth's coronation quite well. It was the same year that I got married. Eighteen I was and Stan my husband was twenty-nine. He took me down to Porthcawl the day after our wedding to celebrate. Do you know what? That was my first time at the sea side. Oh, you're ready now, are you? I do keep on, don't I? I suppose it's because I'm on my own so much that when anyone comes, I can't stop talking. Sorry, Vicar.'

'Please, don't be sorry, Mrs Turvey,' I replied. 'It's always a pleasure to listen to you, but now it's down to business. Let us pray.' She knew the service by heart, which was just as well, because she could not hold a prayer book. I had to communicate her by dipping the wafer into the wine and placing it in her mouth. When I finished she remained silent with her eyes closed for quite a while, as I cleansed the vessels and removed my surplice and stole. Then she looked at me, painfully raising her head a little.

'Thank you, Vicar. That was lovely. I do look forward

to my Communion but I'm afraid I won't be here to have it much more. I know it looks as if I have plenty of breath to talk to you but, when you have gone, there won't be much left. I save it up for when anybody calls. Anyway, I'm more than ready to meet my maker. I've had a good life and now I feel very tired. I'm sure the Lord will soon be saying that my time is up, and I'll be very grateful, believe me.'

The other three parishioners were not as talkative and long before lunchtime I was back at the Vicarage where Eleanor was waiting impatiently to hear about the Bishop's telephone call. Heather Andrews had gone and she was on the doorstep before I could get out of the car.

'Come on, spoilsport,' she said. 'Let's have an account of what his lordship has told you.'

'Hold on, woman,' I replied. 'Keep control of yourself, please.'

'Really, Secombe, you can be most exasperating at times. I'll have to have words with your mother about you.' There was an edge to her voice which indicated that any further delay in imparting the information would be most unwise. With my one arm holding my surplice, and the other arm round her waist, I led her into the house.

'In a nutshell, my love,' I said, 'his lordship has offered me a living.' She stopped suddenly as we were about to enter my study.

'Say that again,' she demanded.

'He has offered me the parish of Abergelly and wants us to see the Vicarage and the church before giving him a reply. I have told him it will have to be a joint decision, because you have your practice here in Pontywen.'

'You can say that again,' she commented forcefully. 'I thought he said to you when he offered you this parish that he wanted someone who would stay here for a long time.'

'I know that, love, but evidently he feels that I am the man who can revive church life in a large parish which has become run down after the present incumbent has been there for nearly forty years. It needs a young man with plenty of energy, and new ideas.'

She cut me short. 'Stop bragging, Secombe. I could say that I have revived a practice after the previous practitioner had been there for nearly forty years. It would hardly be fair to expect me to walk out on it just as I have managed with the help of David Andrews to put it on its feet.'

'Calm down, Eleanor. His lordship said that if I did not wish to leave Pontywen he would understand fully. He just wants us both to have a look at Abergelly and then let him know "in our own good time", to quote him, our decision. So I suppose the least we can do is to drive down to the place, have a word with Canon Morris, look at everything and then report back to him if it is yea or nay.'

She looked at me with narrowed eyelids, a look I had learned to treat with caution. 'I tell you now, it will be nay. By all means let's go down to Abergelly, if that is what he wants. How can you expect me to give up everything I have been trained to do, apart from the financial side of things, to become just a vicar's wife. I am a doctor, Fred, just as you are a vicar. In Pontywen we can be both and live in perfect harmony.' She caught hold of me and held me tight. I raised her head and kissed her.

'My dear love,' I said, 'whatever we do, it will be a mutual decision, you should know that by now. I love Pontywen and its people and so do you. Abergelly will have to be something tremendous to make us change horses.'

'World shattering, I would say,' she replied and returned my kiss.

'I think we should get it over and done with. What about a phone call to Canon Morris and a trip to Abergelly tomorrow morning?' I suggested.

'Agreed,' she said. 'The sooner we get this out of our system the better.'

Once I had taken off my cassock and had been fortified by an aperitif before our lunch of sausage and mash, I rang the Vicar of Abergelly. It was some time before there was an answer.

'Abergelly Vicarage,' said a deep voice at the other end.

'This is Fred Secombe, Vicar of Pontywen,' I replied. 'The Bishop has asked me if I would come down to your parish and have a look around with a view to becoming the next Vicar. Would it be convenient if my wife and I came to Abergelly tomorrow morning? I know it is short notice but we shall not be able to visit the parish until next week, otherwise.'

A silence ensued. 'I should think that will be all right. We are a bit upside down in the Vicarage, getting ready to go in a few weeks' time, but I suppose it is better for you to come now rather than later on when everything will be topsy-turvy. I have heard you have been doing great things at Pontywen. It would be good for Abergelly to have some young blood in the parish. One day, Vicar, you will be old and unable to do what you always found straightforward and easy to do. I have gone long past that stage and if we had been financially situated to have somewhere to live, my wife and I would have gone some time ago. Now we have bought a cottage in Breconshire and we are eager to go, I can tell you.'

The next morning we made our way to Abergelly, a town with a population of ten thousand and the administrative centre for the valley. On the fringes were a large aluminium works, a colliery, and a tinplate works. Amongst its many shops, it boasted a Woolworths store, a Burton's tailoring establishment and a branch of Boots the chemist. It was a thriving place where unemployment belonged to its past and had no part in its present and future. Moreover, its rugby team included Newport and Cardiff in its fixture list. In other words, Abergelly had an importance that Pontywen would never equal.

As I drove through its streets to the Vicarage, I began to feel an urge to become the Vicar of such a hive of activity and to wish that my wife was not a doctor tied to a practice in a less desirable parish. I glanced quickly at Eleanor to see what effect the town was having on her. She had been quiet ever since we entered its environs and now was looking out through the window at the cavalcade of shoppers on the pavements.

'Very busy here,' I ventured to remark. 'It's like Piccadilly Circus compared to Pontywen.'

'Now then, Frederick,' she replied, 'don't start getting big ideas. Pontywen suits me.' A few minutes later, we entered the Vicarage drive through the opened rusty gates which could not have received a coat of paint since Hitler invaded Poland, as I said to Eleanor.

'More like the Kaiser's invasion of Belgium,' she replied.

Abergelly Vicarage was a Victorian building, constructed with stones hewn out of the local quarry, which had also supplied the material for the parish church adjoining it. Both were grey-brown monuments to the lack of taste which afflicted the church architects of the time. They provided an antidote to the ambition which the streets of Abergelly had kindled in my breast. 'This is the reality!' I said to myself. 'This is where I would live and work. This is where my children would be brought up.' The Vicarage at Pontywen was decorated by the elegant lawns which bordered the long drive leading to the front of the house. Here the drive was no more than a few yards long and not a blade of grass was to be seen.

'What a dump!' exclaimed my wife as she got out of the car. 'Living on the main road and listening to the constant noise of the traffic day and night. No, thank you.'

Before I could get to the porch to announce our arrival, Canon Joseph Morris appeared on the doorstep. He was a tall, thin, sallow-faced man with a prominent nose and with a twinkle in his eyes. 'Welcome to Abergelly, Vicar,' he proclaimed in a fruity bass voice which I would have recruited for my Gilbert and Sullivan productions, despite his age. He advanced on Eleanor and shook her hand warmly. 'And a hearty welcome to you, my dear. I understand that you are the local doctor in Pontywen. If you come here I am sure that you will find plenty of work in Abergelly. We are not exactly well blessed with medical care in this town, I'm afraid.'

He led us into the lounge, a large, airy room which

looked out on the hills beyond the town. There were two tea chests in a corner but, apart from that, there was little sign that a removal was imminent. An expensive three-piece suite bordered the big bow windows, flanked by two standard lamps. The centre of the room was occupied by a Persian rug and along the inside wall was a mahogany cabinet surmounted by silverware and an eight-day clock. On either side of the cabinet were two easy chairs with chintz covers. The opulence of the lounge was totally at variance with the impression given by the entrance to the drive. 'Please, sit down and make yourselves comfortable,' he said. 'I'll go and get my wife. She has just come in after her morning's shopping. Would you care for some tea or coffee? It's a little early to offer you anything stronger.'

'Coffee for me,' I replied.

'Ditto!' added Eleanor.

'Strong, weak or indifferent?' asked the Canon.

'We are neither weak nor indifferent,' I said. 'I'm sure my wife will bear me out on that score.'

'You must excuse my husband's bombast, Vicar.' She narrowed her eyes as she looked at me. It was the second time in two days. At that moment Mrs Morris entered the room.

'Edna,' he exclaimed. 'I was just coming to get you from the kitchen. Here are Mr and Mrs Secombe, or should I say Mr and Dr Secombe.'

She was as tall as her husband, a well-preserved lady whose hair still showed signs of the auburn which had given place to grey. Many years younger than the Vicar, she had a ready smile. Dressed in tweeds and wearing a necklace over her brown jumper, she looked more the kind of lady to be seen on the pages of the *Tatler* than those of the *South Wales Echo*.

'How nice to meet you!' she said. Her accent matched her tweeds. It reminded me of Eleanor's mother with her public school background far removed from the ambivalence of the valleys. I wondered how it had managed to survive such a long exposure to her stay in Abergelly.

'They have just expressed a preference for a strong cup of coffee,' said Canon Morris.

'I vote for that,' replied his wife, 'and I expect you do, as well, dear.' She disappeared into the kitchen while her husband proceeded to give us a brief outline of the church history of Abergelly and its contemporary situation. Apparently there was a need for a new church to be built on a post-war council estate. The roof of the parish church was badly in need of repair and the church organ was in a similar state. Attendance at services had been declining and there was an urgent need of a break from the dated pattern of worship which had continued unchanged since the church was built more than a hundred years ago. 'I warn you,' he said, 'if you take this parish on, it will require a lot of guts for you to interfere with the laws of the Medes and Persians and give the services a completely new look. I can tell you this, too, unless you do that the church in Abergelly will end up as an irrelevance in a community which is expanding as each year goes by. Believe me, Vicar, it will be quite a challenge and only a young man like yourself with energy and vision will be able to face up to it.' Mrs Morris appeared with a tray laden with coffee and biscuits as he finished his job description facing the next Vicar of Abergelly.

'I hope you don't find it too daunting, young man, but it is just as well to be honest when describing what is involved. I shall just say one thing more. If you are prepared to accept the challenge, there are quite a number of parishioners who will support you. There are also quite a number of stick-in-the-muds who will say, "As it was in the beginning, is now and ever shall be". However, I am sure that, once the congregation see what you have in mind, you will have more support than opposition. Of that, I am certain.'

'Milk and sugar?' inquired the Vicar's wife. 'That's enough shop for the moment,' she added.

After the light refreshments, we visited the church. Unlike St Mary's Pontywen, St Peter's boasted a tower and a peal of eight bells. It was a large building with a nave which could seat six hundred people and a spacious chancel where an elaborate east window, depicting scenes involving its patron saint, looked down on a sanctuary twice the size of that in my own church. It was most impressive. 'I think a visit to the Waunfelin estate is the next step,' said the Vicar. 'It will give you an idea of the challenge facing you if you come here.' Half an hour later, we were on top of a hill looking down on the town, standing on a derelict patch of land surrounded by numerous rows of newly built terraced barracks, meriting the description of a concrete jungle. There was not a shop to be seen. 'This is to be the site of the new church and a parsonage adjoining it,' announced Canon Morris.

'At the moment, it looks as if any priest coming to live here would be a clerical Robinson Crusoe, stranded in an area of mindless development,' I replied. 'I should imagine that all the inhabitants of these so-called houses must feel that they have been banished into exile. There is no sense of community here whatsoever. It's just a barren wilderness.'

'Now you can see why I called it a challenge,' remarked the old priest quietly. 'Some vicar will have to face it. These people have no facilities of any kind. As you say, there are no shops, no pubs, no meeting place of any kind. There is no doctor's surgery, the nearest is down in the town. That's what I meant, Dr Secombe, when I said that there would be plenty of work for you if you decided to come to Abergelly. You can see, that is no exaggeration.'

As we drove home, we were both silent. I could see that the abandonment of the population of the Waunfelin housing estate presented as much of a challenge to her as it did to me. My wife's sense of vocation was very strong. It was not until we were seated in the lounge of the Vicarage drinking the coffee Mrs Watkins had prepared for us that I broached the subject. 'Well?' I asked. 'Do I phone the Bishop this afternoon and tell him that I am not interested or do we wait a few days to weigh up the pros and cons?'

'Let's put it another way,' she said. 'Are we prepared to become missionaries or are we not? That estate comes into the category of a mission field. I have a well established medical practice here and you have a comfortable living with few problems. We have a nice house and a large garden where our children can run wild as they grow older. At Abergelly Vicarage there is nowhere for them to play.'

'Those are the cons,' I replied. 'Now let's have the pros, if any. As far as I am concerned I would relish the challenge of a large parish. I much prefer the parish church there to ours here. As far as shopping facilities are concerned, there is no comparison with Pontywen. It is a thriving town. If I stay here, I could develop into a turnip.'

'Very funny,' she said. 'To become a turnip is not in your nature any more than it is in mine. Yes, I must admit that I felt a strong urge to get up off my backside and do some pioneering work on that estate.'

'In that case,' I suggested, 'let's think about it for a few days before I let his lordship know about my decision.'

'Done,' she replied.

Two days later Pontywen church hall was full for the rural deanery's venture into sex education. The Mothers' Union groups figured prominently in the audience. There was a sprinkling of men, mainly from our own Saints' Club. Young people were conspicuous by their absence, that is apart from two young curates who had been dragooned into coming by their incumbents. The average age of the clergy present was nearer seventy than sixty. Eleanor had borrowed the blackboard from St Padarn's Sunday School to complement that belonging to the St Mary's Sunday School. Each was decorated by a large anatomical representation of the human body, male and female, supplied by Pontywen Hospital. A sense of excitement mingled with foreboding was in the air when the Rural Dean rose from behind the table at the front of the hall to begin the proceedings. My wife was seated beside him, surveying the elderly assembly in front of her who had come to be instructed in the basics of sexual relations.

'Now then,' began the Rural Dean, 'I am sure we are

all grateful to Dr Secombe for giving of her time to give us this lecture about the – er – way in which God has arranged for our – er – human race to be carried down through the ages. There is nobody better than a doctor to – er – talk about such things but, before she starts, will you all stand for a prayer?' A noisy scraping of chairs on the block floor ensued, drowning the opening words of his address to the Almighty. Even when there was silence for the rest of his prayer, he had rattled through it at such a speed that Eleanor waited until the last chair had come to rest and then stood to address her listeners.

'Mr Rural Dean, fellow Christians,' she began, 'at the beginning of creation, according to the first chapters of the book of Genesis, God created male and female and told them to be fruitful and multiply. This they have done, as the Rural Dean has said, "down through the ages". Tonight we are going to look at the way in which God arranged for this to happen. Here on my left is the anatomy of the female and on my right that of the male. Let us consider first of all the female body.' She then went on to describe in detail the female genitals and the way in which they were connected to the ovary. By now the Rural Dean was showing distinct signs of embarrass-ment. When she turned to the male body, describing the function of the penis, he became acutely uneasy, looking anywhere but at the figure on the blackboard. This disquiet was shared by the Mothers' Union contingent and was further compounded when my wife proceeded to emphasise that the sexual act was not invented by God simply to reproduce the human species but also to give pleasure to those engaged in it. By the time she had elaborated on the way in which this pleasure could be obtained there was an outbreak of coughing and shuffling of chairs. 'Finally,' she said, 'I think it is time that this essential part of human relationships should be brought out into the open. I wonder how many of you who are parents have given any guidance to your children in these matters. So many teenage pregnancies are the result of woeful ignorance on the part of youngsters who know nothing about their bodies. If you want to ask questions on what I have been speaking about, I shall be only too pleased to answer them.'

The Rural Dean was on his feet immediately. 'I am afraid there is no time for questions. If you will all stand, we shall finish with a prayer.' This was said at such a rate that even the Almighty would find it difficult to decipher it. Evidently the dignitary was anxious to escape as quickly as possible, as were the Mothers' Union members. The only listeners were the two curates, who could scarce contain their glee at the discomfort felt by their elders. They thanked Eleanor as they left, the only two to do so.

On the contrary, as the Rural Dean left, he said, 'It is a pity you did not use those lantern slides, Dr Secombe. They were much more suitable for a mixed audience. By the way, my wife and I have been invited to see the coronation at the Mansion with Sir Edward and Lady Davies. So I am afraid we shall not be with you for it!'

When we returned to the Vicarage, Eleanor said to me, 'I have made my mind up. As far as I am concerned I am quite prepared to go to Abergelly. It will be a different rural deanery and not the back woods of the diocese, as this one appears to be. It's now up to you.'

'I am more than ready to move,' I replied, 'but let's sleep on it before I contact the Bishop.'

Next morning, as we enjoyed our morning cup of tea in bed, I asked her if she was still of the same mind. 'I meant what I said last night, Fred. You can phone the Bishop this morning if you want to. I think the Lord has decided it is time for us to go.'

Promptly at nine o'clock I rang his worship to tell him I would accept the living of Abergelly.

'Splendid,' he said, 'both for you and Abergelly.'

12

'Vicar,' said Idris the Milk, 'you can't do this to us! You and Dr Secombe are part of Pontywen. We all thought that you would be here for thirty years or longer, like Canon Llewellyn.'

The news of my appointment to the living of Abergelly had caused consternation in the parish – and not only in the parish but in the surgery. David Andrews told Eleanor that he was 'shell-shocked' for only the second time in his life. The first occasion was during the closing stages of the war. 'That,' he said, 'I was prepared for, but not this. Our partnership is beginning to flourish. We have the monopoly of medical practice in Pontywen.' Had we not been so determined to move, the reaction to the announcement had been so strong that I might have been tempted to withdraw my acceptance of the living.

So we began to make plans for our departure. Eleanor was engaged in negotiating with David over the sale of the practice and also with Abergelly Town Council about the building of a surgery on the Waunfelin housing estate. I had to cope with the disappointment of Emlyn Howells, my curate, the first assistant priest with whom I had any rapport. 'I'm sorry, Emlyn,' I told him, 'that I have to leave so soon after you have come here. Still, you have settled in very quickly and your help will be invaluable to my successor. Who knows, after a couple of years you could come and join me as priest in charge of the Waunfelin estate. You would be the ideal man for that position. In the interregnum you will have plenty of experience of looking after a parish until the new man comes. I hate to think of what would happen to it if Charles Wentworth-Baxter were here.'

It was fortunate that the coronation was imminent and that a frenzy of anticipation had gripped the country. Pontywen was no exception. By now all the arrangements for the parish's celebrations were completed. The eve of the service in Westminster Abbey would be marked by a concert in the church hall featuring the Gilbert and Sullivan Society at the unusually early time of six thirty. Immediately the concert was over, the hall would undergo a quick transformation from a theatre into a dining place for the children of the parish the next day. They were to be regaled with cakes and sandwiches and an endless supply of Emmanuel Thomas's fizzy pop. Then they would parade down to the Welfare Ground where they would be treated to pony rides by Heather Andrews and would take part in races, in which the grown-ups would also participate. That had been the easiest part of the programme to arrange. What had been the most difficult activity to organise was the allocation of television viewers to the only possessors of sets in the parish. As Eleanor said. It was the biggest cross I had been given to bear since I came to the parish, apart from Charles. As far as I was concerned, John Logie Baird had done mankind a great disservice by discovering that it was possible to convey images through the air and into a receptacle in every living room. I could see that once a family could afford to rent a set or pay for one, that box, be it plastic or wooden, would take precedence over any other household appliance, come what may. All I knew was that it was the source of the bitterest animosity I had ever experienced in Pontywen. To that extent it made our departure more desirable.

The morning before the coronation, I went down to the church hall to watch the preparations for the evening's concert. Inevitably it was Bertie Owen who had appointed himself as foreman. When I arrived he was allotting various tasks to the volunteers who had turned up to help. 'Dai and Harry, can you manage to get the piano up on the stage? If you need any extra help, Llew is cleaning the toilets at the moment but I'm sure he'll lend a hand.'

'Hold on, Bertie,' I shouted from the back of the hall, 'that piano stays down on the floor. Didn't you hear Aneurin say that it would take up too much room when everybody is on stage for the choruses? In any case, since when where you given the authority to be ordering people about? I thought Idris had been given that job.'

'Well, as you can see, Vicar,' he retorted, 'he hasn't shown up yet and the sooner things get done the better.'

'It's more than likely that he has been held up on his milk round, as you well know, Bertie. In which case he will be here as soon as possible and I don't think he will take kindly to your butting in.'

At that moment Idris appeared behind me in the doorway. 'Right, Bertie,' he instructed, 'get that coat off and your sleeves rolled up and prepare to sweat a bit for a change. How about starting to unstack the chairs in the cloakroom?' Dai Williams and Harry Evans indulged in a snigger as the would-be foreman took off his coat angrily and glared at Idris, whose five feet five inches had dared to command his six feet one inch. It was a long-running contest which Bertie lost every time.

'Do you want me to render assistance, Idris?' I asked.

'Certainly not, Vicar,' he replied. 'You save all your energy for rendering those duets with your good lady this evening. Since it is the last time we'll have the pleasure of listening to them, you had better make sure they're of top quality. I wouldn't be surprised, by the way, if the Abergelly Operatic put in a bid for your services.'

After watching the hive of activity for half an hour I returned to the Vicarage where I found Jones the Wireless on top of the roof fixing the television aerial to the chimney. We had received the set from my brother a week ago but it was only now that the one and only expert in Pontywen had time to put it in working order, probably because we had not bought the set from him. When I went into the kitchen, I found Eleanor in a state of high indignation. 'Look at this,' she said and thrust a letter into my hand. 'Read it and tell me what you think.' It was on Mothers' Union notepaper and bore the address of the Diocesan President, the Hon. Octavia Jones-Anderson of Hengam Castle.

Dear Dr Secombe,

I have received a number of complaints from members of the Mothers' Union in your deanery. They have asked me to express their concern about your talk on sex education held under the auspices of the Moral Welfare Council of the diocese. Apparently you ignored the approved lantern slides issued by the Council and proceeded to give an exceedingly explicit talk on sexual relations which those present found most offensive. I must remind you that there is a vast difference between an audience of medical students and the Christian lay persons of a typical deanery. I trust that if ever you are invited to address a similar assembly in the future you will temper your remarks accordingly.

Yours truly, Octavia Jones-Anderson, JP.

When I had finished my perusal of the missive I was silent for a moment. 'Well, come on, Secombe,' demanded my wife, 'pronounce judgement.'

'First of all,' I replied, 'I can only say that she had a cheek to write this letter since she was not present to hear you and form her own opinion. Secondly, I am proud to be the husband of someone who has the courage of her own convictions. If you keep on doing that as long as you are my wife, I shall always take my hat off to you.' I caught hold of her and kissed her.

'Hang on, my love,' she replied, 'and what do you mean "as long as I am your wife?" Are you contemplating a change of partner?'

I gave her a hard smack on her bottom. 'You deserve that for such an outrageous suggestion.'

'Only checking,' she said. She decided that she would wait a few days before replying, if only to couch the letter in terms appropriate to the JP's social position.

Early that afternoon, Aneurin Williams, musical director of the Pontywen Gilbert and Sullivan Society, came in to give us a rehearsal of the duets we had to perform that evening. Before he sat down to play he said, 'I feel I have to warn you that you are going to leave chaos behind you in this Society. Not only do we have to find a tenor and soprano lead but we also have to appoint a producer and a chairman of the casting committee. It is going to be mayhem. Either the Bishop will have to appoint an incumbent who has a wife who can sing and who is capable of being a benevolent dictator as you have been or there will be complete disintegration.'

'Come off it,' replied Eleanor, 'who is better to assume the role of the benevolent dictator than yourself? You have all the musical expertise, not to mention the stature of a pillar of the community. You have been musical master at Pontywen Grammar School for the past twenty years or so and, not only that, you have the respect of every member of the Society.'

'There are two things I haven't got,' he said. 'The first is my complete lack of any histrionic ability. The second is my lack of a clerical collar to give me any authority. For those two reasons I predict that there will be squabbles over casting and over the direction by whoever is unfortunate to have to correct the gestures or the interpretations of the principals in the next production. My apologies for beginning our final music rehearsal in such a negative way. Now then, let's get down to work.'

Before we could 'get down to work' there was a ring on the front door. 'Blast!' exclaimed my wife. 'Pardon my language. That must be Ernie Jones, coming to connect the television to the aerial. He said he would be here in the late afternoon. I can't ask him to come back, otherwise we may all be looking at a blank screen tomorrow. He has to bore a hole through the window sill to make the connection. Let me check first.' She made a quick exit to the front door. Back she came accompanied by Ernie.

'Sorry to interrupt your music practice, Vicar, but unless

I do the work now I don't know when I can finish it. I'm up to my eyes in it.'

'I suggest we go down to the church hall,' said Aneurin. Ten minutes later Eleanor and I were launched into the lovely duet from *The Pirates of Penzance*, 'Stay, Frederick, stay'. As we finished it, Aneurin said, 'What could be more appropriate to express the sentiments of your audience tonight?' The second duet we had chosen to sing was the kissing duet between Nanki-Poo and Yum-Yum from *The Mikado*, 'Were you not Ko-ko plighted?'

'If you don't mind my saying so,' said our pianist, 'you couldn't have chosen two more sloppy duets than these.'

'With a wife like mine,' I replied, 'what else would you expect me to choose.'

'Flattery,' said Eleanor, 'can get you anywhere, even as far as Abergelly, and that applies to you, Aneurin. As far as your remark about our first effort is concerned, it's Abergelly here we come, no mistake.'

When we went back to the Vicarage we found Jones the Wireless still in attendance, with his van proclaiming, 'Jones, Wireless and Television suppliers. Beat us if you can.' Since there was no one else in Pontywen to beat him it was a pointless boast. As we entered the sitting room we were confronted with a blur of images which Ernie was trying to focus into something recognisable. 'I may have to adjust the aerial,' he said. 'You are down in a dip here and it makes the reception difficult. It's much better in Ashburnham Close, I can tell you.'

'Well, since we don't live in Ashburnham Close,' my wife replied acidly, 'it is your job to see that we can have a reasonable picture on our set. If you have to twiddle the aerial for the next few hours, you are not going from here until we can at least have some idea of what is supposed to be shown on that screen.'

Jones the Wireless winced at the onslaught. 'Right, Dr Secombe,' he murmured, avoiding her gaze. 'I'll see if I can get it more in line with the transmitter in Cardiff. It's the hills, you see.'

'I don't care if it is Mount Everest,' she exploded, 'at least I am sure that you can do better than that Picasso picture you've got at the moment.'

In the kitchen Mrs Watkins and our nursemaid Marlene were in earnest conversation when we entered. 'I've just been saying to Marlene,' said our daily, 'I expect the children will miss being in this nice big Vicarage and all that lovely garden. Marlene was saying that one in Abergelly is stuck right in the middle of the town with all that traffic and that.' Marlene blushed at being caught talking behind her employer's back. Mrs Watkins had no such inhibitions. As Arthur, our part-time gardener used to say, 'She's like a gramophone record, playing the same old tune but a little bit cracked.'

'Well,' said Eleanor, 'the house in Abergelly is just as big as this one. In fact the downstairs rooms are even a little bigger than in this one. What's more, across the road is a lovely park with a splendid playground for the children – I am more concerned that the children will miss you, Marlene, much more than they will miss the house. The Vicar and I have been talking this over. How would you like to come with us?'

Marlene blushed more than she did at being overheard. 'I'd love to,' she stammered, 'that is if my mother will let me. I'd miss the children so much if I couldn't look after them anymore. In any case, there's nothing to keep me in

Pontywen. There's a lot more going on in Abergelly, like the cinema and the dances in the Welfare.'

'Since we are on this subject,' I added, 'how do you feel, Mrs Watkins, about coming as well? There are six bedrooms in the Vicarage. You would be able to have a sitting room which you could share with Marlene.' The prospect of sharing a sitting room with Marlene did not appeal to her, it was evident.

'Well, thank you, Vicar, but I don't think I can leave Pontywen. I've been here all my life and I'm too old to make a move now. I'm sure there will be plenty of women down there who will be only too glad of a job helping in the Vicarage. It's been lovely being here with you but I think the time has come for me to live on my pension and that. By the way, Dr Secombe, I've just put the sausage rolls in the oven for the television party tomorrow. I thought I would leave the Welsh cakes until first thing in the morning. They are always better when they are made fresh, like.'

'I know that,' I said. 'I used to take them hot from the baking stone when my mother was cooking them.'

'It's no wonder you suffer from indigestion,' remarked my wife. 'Don't you let him do that tomorrow, Mrs Watkins, otherwise he will be disrupting the audience by dashing into the kitchen for some bicarbonate of soda midway through the crowning ceremony.'

At six o'clock we made our way down to the church hall, leaving Marlene in charge of the children. 'Thank God we shall be taking her with us to Abergelly,' Eleanor said. 'The children would be heartbroken if she stayed in Pontywen. Let's hope that her mother will raise no objection. They are a very close family, as you know.'

'I'm sure her mother would rather that she was with us than in a factory,' I replied. The audience was already queueing outside the doors when we reached the hall.

'Hardly surprising,' said my wife, 'when you think it is a free show by the only musical society in the town, and not only that, but one of top quality.'

'Self-praise is no recommendation,' I retorted.

Inside the hall there was the usual chaos as the bow-tied and the pseudo dinner-suited male members of the chorus mingled on the stage with the young ladies, who were clad in a variety of attire which encompassed the tasteful and the positively garish. All were excited as if they were on some kind of outing. As Idris the Milk remarked about the last-night performance of *The Pirates of Penzance*, 'the adrenalin was overflowing'. The Secombe era had reached its grand finale. In view of the coronation, it could be described as its crowning glory. I mentioned this to my wife as I watched the antics on the stage. 'Big head,' she said.

In front of a full house with latecomers standing at the back of the hall I stood in front of the curtains to introduce the concert. 'I am proud to present the finest operatic society in the Valley' (cheers) 'who are to entertain you this evening. They will present excerpts from their great successes over the past five years from *The Pirates of Penzance* to *The Mikado*, and here to conduct the chorus and principals is the musical director and their inspiration, Mr Aneurin Williams!' Aneurin came forward and took his bow amidst great applause. He beckoned to his talented student at the piano, David Protheroe, graduate with distinction RAM, and the roof was raised with a spirited rendering of 'Dance a Chachucha' from *The*

Gondoliers. Then came Iorwerth Ellis, my tenor under-study since the inception of the society, desperate to prove his worthiness as my successor. He sang 'Is life a boon?' from *The Yeoman of the Guard*. He had a fine tenor voice but no histrionic ability. It would have been better if he had confined himself to his singing but he attempted some inappropriate gestures which seemed to indicate that he was a puppet whose manipulator had not read the script. However, his singing won the day and he received a warm round of applause. Next came Idris the Milk accompanied by the chorus, who sang the famous song from *The Pirates of Penzance*, where the sergeant of police complains about his unfortunate vocation, 'A policeman's lot is not a happy one'. To this he added a third verse: 'When our Vicar's got a living in the offing and decides his days in Pontywen are done. When his missis tires with coping with the endless coughing which plagues her waiting room from ten to one, she thinks the time has come to be a mother. By looking after both her daughter and her son. Ah, take one consideration with another, a warden's lot is not a happy one.' This piece of doggerel was the hit of the evening and had a reception which was even more rousing than that for our duets.

It was a happy evening which ended all too soon and was followed by a frantic transformation of the hall into a suitable venue for the beanfeast to come next afternoon. Tables were laid and were decorated with the coronation mugs that the organising committee had bought for the children. Agnes Collier was on her best behaviour in charge of the kitchen and twice managed to control her temper when Bertie Owen tried to invade her realm. As

Idris said, 'It is a landmark in their relationship.' Then he added, 'Mind, I hope he keeps out of her way tomorrow.'

When we came back to the Vicarage, we found Marlene watching the television in the sitting room. Ernie had succeeded in producing a 'reasonable' picture as requested by Eleanor. The definition was not of the best but since the landscape of Pontywen was not very cooperative that was not his fault. Our babysitter thought the picture was 'wonderful' and could not wait for tomorrow to come. After going to bed, we talked long into the night, so much had happened in the course of just a few days that our heads were in a whirl. It would not be long before we would be leaving Pontywen for ever. I began to wonder what the churchwardens would be like and whether they would be cooperative. The present Vicar seemed to indicate that there were a fair number of backwoodsmen in the parish who would not take kindly to changes of any kind. What was more disturbing was the disinclination of the Town Council to be helpful to Eleanor in her negotiations for the building of a surgery on the Waunfelin estate. We talked ourselves to sleep.

We awoke to the sound of Elspeth crying in the next room. Eleanor jumped out of bed and pulled back the curtains to reveal a sunny June day. She went off to the nursery singing, 'Oh, what a beautiful morning'. I arose, put on my dressing gown and was about to go downstairs to make the tea when my wife returned, cradling the baby who was still crying loudly.

'I take back what I was singing. I am afraid, my love, that she has all the symptoms of parotitis.'

'What on earth is that?' I asked. 'Is it dangerous?'

'Not particularly,' she said. 'In other words, your daughter has mumps. Her glands are swollen and obviously painful and she has a high temperature.'

'I remember having that when I was about seven or eight and it certainly was painful. I looked like Fatty Arbuckle. When my mother brought me a mirror to look at myself, I started to laugh and cause myself even more pain.'

'It's just as well that you had it then because if you contracted it at your age it could affect your virility. It is quite contagious. Fortunately, like you, I had it in my early childhood. I hope Marlene is the same, otherwise she will have to stay away until they are getting over it. You hold the patient, while I go to see whether David is in the same boat.'

Nothing I could do would pacify Elspeth. If anything she was exercising her lungs more fully than ever. Eleanor came back with the news that our son was affected by the same bug. 'Do you think that we should cancel the television jamboree?' I asked.

'As long as the children are quarantined upstairs I should think it would be all right. The only question mark is Bronwen and her brood. If they haven't had mumps, there might be an element of risk. I'll phone her and ask her if she is prepared to take a chance. You know how devoted she is to her family.'

After we had drunk our quota of morning tea, she telephoned the Wentworth-Baxter household – I was getting ready to take Matins, putting on my cassock and standing alongside her as she rang – she pulled a face when the call was answered by her *bête noire*. 'Could I speak to Bronwen, please?' she inquired. She put her hand over the phone as she waited to speak to Mrs W-B.

'He's hardly full of the joys of spring,' she commented. When his wife came on at the other end a long conversation ensued which was still continuing as I left the Vicarage. There was a handful of parishioners stand outside the porch when I made my way up the church path.

'Mr Howells has gone round to the vestry, Vicar,' said Agnes Collier, whose name had been at the top of the list of potential viewers at our house. The next minute the door was opened and the small congregation trooped into the chancel for the service.

'Have you had mumps?' I asked Emlyn in the vestry. He looked at me quizzically.

'That is a strange question this time of the morning, Vicar,' he replied. 'As a matter of fact I have. I had it when I was five and it came upon me on my birthday and spoilt it. Why do you ask?'

'In that case you will have a permit to view the coronation without any threat to your manhood.'

'You say the strangest things, Vicar. Would you mind explaining yourself?'

'David and Elspeth have chosen to mark the coronation by going down with mumps. According to my wife, if you had not suffered from it, you would have been in danger of impaired virility by being in contact with a stricken household. So, my dear Emlyn, I look forward to your company this morning if only to offset the effect of being in the presence of Bertie Owen and his wife, Agnes Collier, the formidable Mrs Davies in her wheelchair and possibly your predecessor the Reverend Charles Wentworth-Baxter.'

'I think I would rather have the mumps,' he said.

When I arrived at the Vicarage after the service, Marlene opened the door to me before I could put my key in it. 'I saw you coming, Vicar,' she said, 'so I thought I would beat you to it.'

'This means you have had the mumps, I take it, and what is more that your mother has said that you can come with us to Abergelly.'

'That's right and I'm so excited. Mind, I'm sorry about Elspeth and David but I'll look after them, I really will.'

'I'm sure you will, Marlene. Now then, where is my wife?'

'She's in the kitchen with Mrs Watkins and they're making sandwiches for the people coming to see the coronation.'

'A word with you in the study,' Eleanor said as I came through the door. 'I'm afraid I have had bad news from your ex-curate,' she informed me when we were on our own.

'You surprise me,' I replied.

'Bronwen decided that she would rather miss the coronation on television and listen to it on the wireless to avoid any risk of her children getting mumps. Dear Charles was most upset, like the spoilt child that he is. He has not had parotitis. However, he's coming solo, despite the possibility of contracting it. I would suggest that some time during the viewing we bring Elspeth down and place her in his lap. If it means that he could become sterile, we should be doing Bronwen the greatest of favours, don't you agree?'

'I agree on that,' I replied, 'but I don't see why we should inconvenience our daughter to that extent. Let's hope a stray germ invades the room and nobbles him.'

By the time all our guests were crammed into our

sitting room, where the seating capacity had been augmented by chairs borrowed from the church hall, there was an audience of twenty to watch the birth of the new Elizabethan age. Fitting Mrs Davies's wheelchair into a convenient position had been the bone of contention. She

had insisted on having her chair centrally placed at the front, which meant that half a dozen viewers behind her had either to develop swan-like necks or see nothing. Eleanor solved this problem by importing the lectern platform from the church to the back of the room, setting up Edwina on high, a position greatly to her liking. Bertie Owen had been comparatively silent from the moment he had entered the Vicarage. This phenomenon was due to the fact that he was accompanied by his wife, a little women of forbidding appearance, with penetrating blue eyes. She had but to say 'Herbert' to bring him to heel at once. Idris the Milk said it was a pity she wasn't a churchgoer. 'Can't you get her confirmed, Vicar?' he said, after one bad burst of 'Bertieitis'. 'The congregation would double your Easter offering if you managed that.'

Charles was seated next to Emlyn Howells. 'It's a cross you have to bear just for a few hours,' I told my curate. 'I had to carry it for nearly four years.' There was an air of great excitement as the television cameras showed the crowds along the route to Westminster Abbey and then the honoured guests assembled in the great church.

'I remember King Edward the Seventh's coronation,' announced Edwina.

'Are you sure it wasn't Queen Victoria's?' inquired Agnes Collier, who voted Conservative and had no time at all for a woman who was a prominent member of the local Labour Party. 'Anyway,' she went on, 'I don't know why you're here. I remember you in the thirties when you said you'd like to see the Red Flag flying over Buckingham Palace.'

'Look here, Aggie,' shouted Edwina, 'if it wasn't for being stuck in this wheelchair, I'd give you more than a piece of my mind. Everybody's entitled to change their view.'

By now there were loud protests from some of the viewers that they couldn't hear what Richard Dimbleby was saying because of the noise from the back. 'Ladies!' I said. 'That's enough of that. I suggest we watch in silence from now on and enjoy the spectacle on the screen.'

At this stage of the proceedings, Eleanor and Mrs Watkins came into the room with the light refreshments to be enjoyed before the service began. Sandwiches and Welsh cakes were passed around, together with cups of coffee and tea. Inevitably it was Charles who found he could not balance his plate of sandwiches on his lap without dropping it on the floor. In stooping down to retrieve it and its contents he jerked Emlyn's elbow as he was about to drink his cup of coffee. The curate's best suit was drenched with the hot liquid. 'Charles!' exclaimed my wife. 'For heaven's sake watch what you're doing. Trust you to do something like this.'

'I am not staying here to be insulted,' he said. The two clergymen rose simultaneously, the one to go to the kitchen for running repairs and the other to go out through the door in high dudgeon and speed off up the drive with a roar of the engine which drowned the commentary on the television set.

Bertie Owen spoke for the one and only time during the morning. 'Thank God for that,' he said. After receiving one of his wife's special looks he turned his attention to his cucumber sandwich.

A little later Emlyn left the Vicarage to go back to his house and change his suit. He was back in time to see the beginning of the service. As I opened the door to him I whispered, 'I told you Charles was a cross you had to bear for a few hours; you were lucky. It was less than an hour.'

'You have my sympathy, Vicar. Job pales into insignificance compared with you.'

From then on there was a reverent silence as the coronation service unfolded the secrets of its ancient ritual before the gaze of millions of Her Majesty's subjects who were privileged to watch what had been the prerogative of the few hitherto. When the young woman's head was crowned by the Archbishop of Canterbury both Edwina and Aggie were at one in their appreciation of the solemnity of the occasion. There were further refreshments as the Abbey bells rang out and the impressive cavalcade of regal pomp made its way back to Buckingham Palace. When the programme came to an end, Agnes Collier was first out of the room to dash down to the church hall to supervise the children's tea. As we surveyed the chaos left after the last viewer had gone, Eleanor said, 'What a relief that we don't have to take David and Elspeth to the jamboree this afternoon. At least we shall be able to clear up at our leisure, the three of us females, that is. You can go down to the hall and do your Father Christmas act by all means. My only regret is that David will not be able to have a ride on Heather's pony. He was so looking forward to it.'

'In a week or so's time, my love, I'm sure that Heather will give him a ride on her pony and, what's more, he won't have to queue for it,' I replied.

After I had presided at the children's tea, I went down to the Welfare Ground where Heather Andrews was about to cope with a long queue of children eager for a ride on Daisy, her pony. 'Where's David?' she asked.

'In bed with mumps,' I said, 'so please can you give him a ride on Daisy when he's up and about once again.'

'My dear Fred, he can have as many rides as he likes, you know that. By the way, we enjoyed our viewing of the coronation with the Nicholls. They did us proud. How did your lot like it?'

'Apart from Charles, who left in a huff, they loved it,' I replied.

'What was that all about?' she inquired.

'Over nothing, really,' I said. 'Just another Wentworth-Baxter episode.'

Later that evening Eleanor and I looked out of David's bedroom window to see if there was any sign of the fireworks display on the Welfare Ground. Our son was awake and had been crying with the pain of his ailment. Suddenly a fusillade of rockets shot up into the dying sunlight of 2 June. 'Come on, David,' said my wife, 'and watch the fireworks, or, to use your father's expression, "the crowning glory", ending the Secombe era and beginning the Elizabethan era.'